M000202746

COMMERCIAL FOODS EXPOSED!
And How To Replace Them

By
Gaye Deamer

Published by

D. Publishing
851 So. Lakeview Dr.
Bountiful, Utah 84010

Printed in U. S. A.

ISBN 0-89036-043-X

Fourth Printing,   March 1999

To my wonderful parents

Lyle and Ina Deamer

who exemplify faith, wisdom, courage, honesty and vitality
and who have taught me all the physical and spiritual facets of
living joyfully.

ACKNOWLEDGEMENTS

In producing this book, I would like to express my deepest gratitude:

—To   Robert L. Horsley, for his encouragement and patience in this unbelievable task, and for his tolerance with astronomical expense in doing the research, developing many of the recipes, and completing this work.

—To my children, Heidi and Michael, for their helpful suggestions and creative ideas in developing the recipes, and for their patience and willingness in helping with so many extra household duties.

—To Helen Klann, for her patience and perseverance in typing the manuscript and for her helpful suggestions in general.

—To Marion Law, former assistant to President Ernest L. Wilkinson of Brigham Young University and owner of Malco Sales Executive Enterprises, for the many painstaking hours he spent in critiquing the manuscript, and helping with the documentation.

—To Robert Koropp, the best photographer in the business.

—To John Hawkes, of Hawkes Publishing Inc., for his enthusiasm over this research, and for his assistant, Gene Westover, and others not mentioned for helping with the publication.

—To Dr. Richard Conway; Dr. George Reinbold; Dr. Lindsey Curtis; Dr. Lester Carlson; Dairy Scientist, LeRoy Zaeski; Carol Haught Darling, Colorado Dairy Council; Alice Brace, Colorado State University Extension Service; Carol Sundberg, Colorado Wheat Council; and many other experts in various fields, whose names and places of employment could not be mentioned. To them I give my deepest appreciation.

—To Lyle and Ina Deamer, Everett and Rae Horsley, Robert and Jean Bigler, Charles Carver, Janet Knowles, LaRita Aldredge, Elsie Cooper, LeAnn Garfield, Venie Zier, Peggy Sorenson, Arlene Bishop, Sandy McCall, Maxine Bridger, Marion Nance, Patti Udy, Myrna Dreibellis, Irene Tischer, Anne Tippets, Angela Ford, Gloria Jensen, Pam Vandernakker, Zoetta Paxman and members of the Arvada 1st Ward for their encouragement and help given in various ways.

—To many others not mentioned but who contributed in some way to make this book possible.

INTRODUCTION

When I first decided to write this book, I was very excited about the prospect of offering material that would help educate the public concerning a subject that people were suspicious of, but knew little about. But as I delved deeper into the research, I felt a sense of despair, realizing some people would feel discouraged and helpless. Because commercial foods do have problems and we have to eat many of them to survive. Numerous times I considered giving up the project.

But the more knowledge I gained on the subject, the more the information benefited me, my family and hundreds of other concerned people. The knowledge actually freed me. I shopped more wisely, cooked more nutritiously and noticed a dramatic improvement in the way I felt....The decision was, if the information benefited so many people, it should be completed—which was an unbelievable task.

This book is not intended to turn you into food faddists or neurotic shoppers. (Have you heard the latest Mabel? We've got to stop eating!) It is offered to educate you concerning foods, so when you have choices you can make the best ones.

In order to eat nutritiously, you don't have to go overboard; just use good judgement. Experience tells me, if I refused to let my family indulge in commercial treats etc., occasionally, they'd eat twice as many of them behind my back....I have a friend whose mother would punish her everytime she was caught eating candy. She now eats it for breakfast, lunch and dinner....My advice is "Easy Does It!"

In dealing with the situation, in our family we try to be flexible....When we eat out, anywhere, we eat what's available. If we are served pork sausage casserole, with white rolls, and chocolate cake; that's what we eat. If we go out for ice cream and the children want Brownie Fudge Ice Cream, they may have it. I just try to avoid having this type of food in the home.

I'm not a food faddist, and I buy some commercial foods, but our goal as a family is to become self-sufficient. Being self-sufficient doesn't appear to be a practical goal for everyone, but my feelings are, if people don't work toward this end, they just may not survive the increasing food crisis...increasing "commercial food problems" and the possibility of "no food at all."

This book has been checked by many experts in the fields of Foods, Nutrition, Biochemistry, English, etc., and they have differing opinions (many experts actually disagree with each other).

Some experts feel commercial foods are safer than they've ever been, because scientific research doesn't prove otherwise. The fact is, not enough scientific research is done in this area. The funds just aren't available. One example...there are over 3,000 additives in commercial-type foods. The government has provided funds to have 100 of them checked for safety—while we blindly consume the other 2900. I'm not criticizing the government for this, I'm just revealing that sufficient money isn't available for adequate consumer protection.

We consume over 4 pounds of additives a year; if we consumed that amount at once, they would kill us. Speculation is that they may just be doing that by injecting small amounts over a number of years. A few years ago, we ate only two pounds of additives a year; now it's four; next year it could be five; the next year it could be six. It's a serious problem that cannot be overlooked.

Health problems in the United States, clearly acknowledge we're doing something wrong, and there's proof in this book that our life span hasn't increased. Heart disease, cancer, mental illness and new undiagnosed problems are threatening the lives of Americans at alarming rates. Read the obituaries and observe the number of men who are dying between the ages of 30 and 40. It's frightening!

As the author of this research, my goal in having this book published is summed up in the words of Dr. Oscar Sussman, D.V.M., M.P.H., of the New Jersey Public Health Association. In the Feb. 19, 1971 issue of American Public Health Association's *Nation's Health* Dr. Sussman said:

> *The consumers of the United States have grown up. They should no longer be treated as babies, or imbeciles. True facts should be given to them in all cases with regard to foods, drugs and the enviornment. When given all the facts we can depend on our consumers to properly evaluate them and take action to protect themselves.*

If you use this material as it is intended, it can be a valuable guide in having improved health and it can be a valuable tool for stretching your food dollar....

NOTE TO MY READERS

The request for my book has dramatically increased because of fear of possible world chaos....I was going to revise the entire manuscript to update information and to enhance the book grammatically, but amazingly, there has been very little change in the commercial food chain. In fact, it has become worse. A positive change however, has taken place in the labeling. Labels are now required to have more detailed information so hopefully we can shop more wisely. But commercial foods have not changed, so rather than spend the months it would take to revise the book with the same information with new sources warning of the same problems I uncovered years ago, I want to spend my time more judiciously by helping people become more self sufficient because analysts are warning that we could have some major changes take place, that could rock the world. We hope the analysts are wrong, but all indications point to world-wide calamity.

This book has 280 pages of in-depth information on commercial foods, what to buy, how to preserve and prepare every food imaginable, and how to preserve a garden. Plus recipes are included to make almost every food in the grocery store. The book also teaches people how to improve their health and how to become self sufficient by preserving food and nutrition. I removed the colored pictures in the front of the book to allow space to give you additional information on food and water storage and survival that will assist you in organizing the needs of your family. My goal is to reach as many people as possible.

A commercial food note--There have been new additives on the market that are a real concern. One is Aspartame, or NutriSweet. I don't think we have seen the possible serious side effects of this product. The greatest danger could be that people drink it by the gallons. People who give this to their children could be putting the children at risk. (As an adult, if you are going to drink it–go easy.)

Another product concern is Olestra. Olestra is a fat replacement that tastes like fat but is not a fat-- added to potato chips and other products so products can be labeled as fat free. Olestra interferes with the absorption of fat soluble vitamins A,D,E and K. Eat foods with reduced fat rather than foods with ingredients that interfere with natural bodily processes. Do not give these products to children....Back to family preparedness.

Do you recall the Biblical instruction the Lord gave Noah when he told him to build an Ark in preparation for the devastating flood that would virtually destroy every living thing on the earth. Noah obeyed and he was mocked and laughed at as he built the Ark and as he obediently filled the Ark with everything necessary for the inhabitants of the earth to survive....<u>We do not anticipate another devastating flood. We do however, anticipate another type of possible devastation. My goal is help families become safe.</u>

 <u>I would like to give each family an Ark. And every week I encourage you to put something in the Ark</u> If an emergency arises and food shortages are triggered as anticipated, people will panic and the store shelves could become empty within a few hours. Please start now and put something in your Ark every week. When an item goes on sale buy a case–and buy a variety of foods. Also buy some foods you can eat out of a can–buy a manual can opener. If you have money in savings it might be wise to take some money out of savings and buy a year's supply of food and other commodities your family might need. Don't buy items your family will not use. Shop wisely. How will your family stay warm? Experts advise against buying generators, because you do not need electricity, you need heat and light. You should obtain space heaters, kerosene heater, candles, wood burning stoves, etc.

Imagine if you wake up tomorrow and there's no heat, no lights, no telephone (also no 911), no T.V., no gas for your car, no safe water coming out of your tap because the water sanitation system is run by computers, plus there are no groceries, no toilet paper, no diapers, no medicine and you can't use your toilet because it won't flush. Plus you can't write a check or use your bank card because the banks aren't functional. What do you do?

YOU PREPARE!!! PREPARE!!! PREPARE!!! NOW!!!

In preparation for any disaster the five most important things you can have are:

--a storage of water
--a storage of food
--sources of heat
--sources of light
--some cash

You are encouraged to get enough food storage for one year in case of any emergency. Store foods, etc. in a cool, dry place if possible, but remember that any food is better than no food at all.

Listed below: **FOOD STORAGE NEEDED FOR ONE YEAR.**
THESE ARE QUANTITIES FOR ADULTS. IT IS ADVISED TO COUNT CHILDREN AS ADULTS: The amounts are calculated in pounds.

Wheat–300 lbs.
Nonfat dried milk–85
Sugar and/or honey–45
Salt–5
oils, shortening–30
Grains (rice, oats, corn, barley, millet, etc.)--90
Dried beans, peas, soybeans, lentils, etc–25
Peanut Butter–10
Variety of vegetables, also fresh–100
Potatoes–50
Variety of canned fruit juices–25
Variety of fruits (fresh equivalent)–100
Variety of gelatin, jello, tapioca, chocolate, margarine, butter, powdered eggs, etc.–15
Variety of canned meats–50
Multi Vitamins (365 tablets)
Vitamin C (at least 365 tablets)

Other items you should have–extra needs for babies:(oil, powder, salve, formula, diapers, etc.) Then adhesive tape, bandages, aspirin, alcohol (rubbing), band aids, batteries, and recharger device, blankets and bedding, boric acid, candles, soap, ammonia, cleanser, chorine bleach for water purification and disinfecting, Lysol, disinfectant, extra clothing, yardage, cold remedies, combs, brushes, cooking needs, manual can opener, cookstove (camping equipment is excellent), cotton balls, Q-Tips, deodorant, disposable diapers, dish clothes and towels.

Also dishwashing soap, disinfectants, Epsom salts, manual egg beater, first aid kit and manual, flashlight and extra batteries, foil, fuses, wax paper, garbage can and lid, gauze, hand grinder for wheat, lotion, hair clippers, hot water bottle, Iodine, anti-acid tablets, Kleenex, knives, laxatives, light bulbs, matches (some in sealed metal container).

Milk of Magnesia, mouse traps, prescriptions, drug ointments, grocery bags, paper towels, newspapers, paper cups, napkins and plates, pencils and pens, rags (clean), razor blades, rope, salt, seeds, sewing supplies, (buttons, needles, pins, scissors, sewing machine needles, snaps and hooks, thread, zippers, etc.) Shampoo, sheets, (used sheets can be torn in strips for bandages if heated in the oven.) Shaving needs, soap, soda, toilet tissue, thermometers, tools (axe, hammer, nails, pliers, saw, screwdriver and screws, shovel, hoe, etc.) Toothbrush, toothpaste (or use mixture of 1/4 salt and 3/4 soda), toothpicks, towels and cloths. Other needs: Tweezers, Vaseline, vitamins and vitamin C (rotate and keep in a cool dark place), washboard, water, writing paper and envelopes, foods with medicinal uses (baking soda, baking powder, cornstarch, vinegar, iodized salt). Bicycle, roller skates, etc.

Store water and buy food and medical supplies first to sustain life, then add the other items to your list. The best method to evaluate this extensive list of items you need to be prepared, is to make a vertical column listing each item, then add a column for AMOUNT NEEDED, and a column for AMOUNT ON HAND. Then fill in the numbers with a pencil. When the AMOUNT NEEDED has been purchased and stored the column amounts should match.

WATER STORAGE SAFETY TIPS–Every person needs 8 gallons of water a week for food preparation, drinking and minimal personal hygiene. However, one quart of water or other safe liquid could sustain life...A healthy person can live 3 weeks or longer without food, but they can only live a few days without water. Water storage is inexpensive, but critical. Regardless of your space, start filling clean empty food containers with water. Water can be stored in metal (stainless steel preferred), glass or plastic containers. A metallic taste can be detected in some metal containers and chlorine should not be added to metal containers prior to storage, it can cause corrosion. Glass containers break, so store them on lower shelves–just try to protect them from breaking. Glass is non-permeable to vapors and gases–however vapors and gases can penetrate plastic; water stored in glass or plastic containers should not be stored near gasoline, kerosene, pesticides or similar substances. Any clean plastic or glass container that has had food in it can store water. Empty clean, plastic pop bottles or milk containers work. Pop bottles often just need a hot sudsy rinse. Put a little chlorine bleach in an empty milk carton and fill with water. Let stand for a few hours then clean with sudsy water. An unclean milk container filled with water is not safe but it is an excellent container if clean. Chlorine bleach containers are preferred water storage for washing–some recommend for them for drinking, but I would use them last in an emergency–we do have to wash, so that would be my preference. Plastic containers should be stored out of direct sunlight as the sun can damage plastic. Make certain all lids are clean. Remove any cardboard inserts in the lids as they can house unwanted bacteria. Water from your tape has enough chlorine in it to keep your stored water safe for many months. Store in any clean food container you can find. If you suspect there will be a water problem, fill up your bathtub, buy a tight-fitting rubber stopper if your tub leaks. Know where your inside main water tap is and turn it off immediately so you can safely use the water from your water heater, water softener and toilet tank. Boil water briskly for 5 minutes if it is unsafe to drink or add 4 drops chlorine bleach to each quart water and let it sit for 30 minutes before drinking. Water purification tablet are available–real labels. Check expiration dates, as these tablets expire....If stored water tastes flat just pour it back and forth to aerate and it will taste fine. If water is cloudy chlorine treatment is not recommended. Also, there is no effective way to decontaminate water which contains radioactive or chemical fallout. This has to be supervised by local or state officials.

My hope for you and your family is you have clean, safe water, good nutritious food to eat, warmth, and that you have plenty of light in your life. Realizing that non-electrical light can come from lanterns and candles but knowing most assuredly that the greatest light of all is that glorious light that comes from above.

Gaye Deamer

TABLE OF CONTENTS

Part 1

Food Problems

Aren't Only

in the Foods

Food Problems are Not Only in the Food!

Many Food Experts are Bought and Paid For....

One disheartening fact that emerged about the food industry, is that many questionable products, regardless of safety, are placed on the market....MONEY IS THE SECRET.

Some reputable doctors and food experts are paid astronomical fees to push a product or to make false claims; others are given executive positions in large food industrial firms. Some inspectors will put their inspection stamp on deteriorating or inferior food for a price. Deceptive reports are written for big payments. Untrue claims are made if paid. Almost anything can be be done if the *price is right*....The poor unknowing consumers digest the information, digest the food, and wonder why they don't feel well—while money-hungry experts walk around with padded pockets.

How the Big Food Industries Discredit People Who Try to Expose Them!!

You will notice that people who try to help the deplorable food situation, according to the *mad manufacturers* use *scare tactics* and are *food faddists, health food nuts, or quacks*. If you delve deep enough into food research you will find that these *nut titles* were actually invented by the food manufacturers to discredit people who are trying to inform the people as to what is going on. One food expert said to me, "You're really in an enviable position to write such a book because you're not a food faddist, and you have no ten-year-title or university position to defend." Maybe I am, but I'm certain they will think of something, because these food manufacturers are very clever people. Clever enough to deceive millions and millions of Americans.

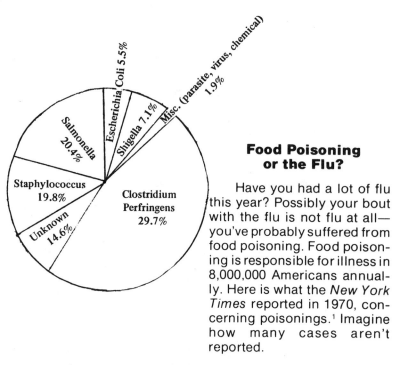

Food Poisoning or the Flu?

Have you had a lot of flu this year? Possibly your bout with the flu is not flu at all—you've probably suffered from food poisoning. Food poisoning is responsible for illness in 8,000,000 Americans annually. Here is what the *New York Times* reported in 1970, concerning poisonings.[1] Imagine how many cases aren't reported.

Common Food Poisonings

Clostridium perfringens—Most common food is reheated cooked meats; incubation period 8 to 24 hours; symptoms include diarrhea, abdominal cramps; symptoms usually gone after 8 hours.

Staphylococcus—Most common foods are custard and cream filled bakery products; also ham, tongue, processed meats, cheese, ice cream, potato salad, hollandaise sauce, chicken salad, incubation period 1 to 6 hours; symptoms include severe and sudden abdominal cramps, nausea, vomiting and diarrhea; recovery in 6 to 8 hours.

Salmonella—Most common foods are poultry, eggs, and products with dried eggs such as cake mixes; incubation period 8 to 24 hours; symptoms include nausea and vomiting followed by chills, high fever; symptoms may persist for two weeks; sometimes fatal to infants and elderly.

Shigella—Most common foods are milk and ice cream, but may also include food contaminated by infected workers in food plants or by bacteria-laden insects; incubation period up to 48 hours; symptoms include severe diarrhea, abdominal cramps, mild fever; symptoms usually last several days.

Escherichia coli—Most common foods include shellfish and sewage—contaminated water used in food processing; incubation period 6 to 24 hours; symptoms include cramps, diarrhea, nausea, vomiting; symptoms usually subside in 6 to 8 hours.

"Mad Scientists?" You Decide!

Authors Gene Marine and Judith Van Allen freely call commercial food technologist and manufacturers "Mad Scientists" because in offering enticing foods for public consumption they throw in ingredients such as dyes, bleaches, antioxidants, emulsifiers, preservatives, flavors, buffers, noxious sprays, acidifiers, alkalizers, deodorants, drying agents, moisteners, gases, thickeners, disinfectants, extenders, defoliants, fungicides, neutralizers, sweeteners, anticaking and antifoaming agents, conditioners, curers, hydrolizers, hydrogenators, maturers, fortifiers, reversers and many others....Somebody must be mad, because many of the above additives are extremely harmful and can actually cause death.

Are We Really Living Longer Today?

Afraid Not!! Life expectancy figures have nothing to do with how long people actually live. The figures are an average of the ages of people who die in a given year. It has absolutely nothing to do with health and longevity. When people claim we're more healthy than we've ever been, that's just not true.

Life expectancy, a few decades ago was much lower than it is today, only because more babies died in infancy. This is what lowered the over all figures.

In a 1968 report, 20.9 percent more babies survived than did in 1900. This is why life expectancy has jumped; not because we're living longer.

Let's say by pretending, that 85 per cent of our population were stricken with an incurable disease, but the other 15 percent cared for them so well that nobody died that year. For that particular year our life expectancy would climb to a record all-time high—with a sickly population....Life expectancy figures just aren't accurate.

Why Some Families Possibly Have
the Same Health Problems

Speculation is that possibly the reason some health problems are dominant in certain families is because of the way they eat. Possibly there are some nutritional deficiencies being passed from one generation to another; such as in food selection and care, cooking methods, and food preferences. Could this be the reason for health problems being prevelent in mothers, then daughters, etc.?

Be aware that some deficiencies take years and years to take their deadly toll. Total education in foods and nutrition should be mandatory for high school students, including boys, because many health problems are being blamed on poorly educated people with regards to this area.

Americans—the Human Guinea Pig

Are you aware that Canada and many of the European countries will not allow many of our foods imported into their countries because they are considered *unsafe*. We the American people are actually being used as *human guinea pigs,* as 90 percent of the foods we eat are never checked for safety. Most ingredients are allowed in foods, unless proven to be detrimental through public use. And even when some ingredients are proven hazardous it almost takes an act of Congress to get them removed.

Many harmful ingredients in food aren't exposed because they fear *public panic,* which would be detrimental to the economy. A healthy economy full of unhealthy people doesn't make sense.

Changes are Made From Public Pressure

Public pressure is one effective way the consumer has of making positive changes. Start complaining! You don't have to turn into a radical to demand some changes. But the more letters you write and the more groups you form, the more you will see action. Let's demand absolutely every ingredient be listed on labels including labels on meat, produce, dairy products, canned foods, etc., in places where it can be readily seen and understood. I'd like to enjoy my baked potato knowing that it isn't filled with antisprouting chemicals and that my cottage cheese doesn't have ingredients such as sodium hypochlorite and cochineal (dried insects). Groups, clubs, organizations and individuals can actually change the food situation. Start today! The health of you and your family is your reward. Read on and see why we must have some changes....

Part 2

Those

Adulterated

Dairy Products

What About Milk?

Most of us don't have to be told about the value of milk in our diet. Milk is a very nutritious food, and is an excellent source of complete protein having a high 82 value of NPU (Net Protein Utilization). Milk is an excellent drink, of course, but it can also be used in soups, sauces, ice creams and puddings; or made into yogurt, soft cheese, hard cheese, cottage cheese, sour cream, and buttermilk.

Yet milk is a very controversial food. You hear all types of pros and cons concerning milk: Should we drink it? Is it really good for us? Does it contribute to body cholesterol? How much should we have? Is raw milk safe to drink?

Here are some facts:

Raw Versus Pasteurized Milk

Milk used to be considered one of nature's most perfect foods and it still sits high on the totem pole of valuable foods if its in the *raw* (unpasteurized) *state.* Raw milk is a wonderful, natural life-giving food. The difficulty is finding it. Present day pasteurized milk is not the near perfect food that raw milk is. For the high heat required for pasteurization not only kills germs, it also destroys a lot of the precious food value.

Pasteurization along with homogenization destroys most of the lipids (lecithin) found in raw milk. (Lecithin is a natural cholesterol fighter.) This high heat also destroys vital amounts of the milk's vitamin C, A and B; calcium and other vital nutrients. It has been reported that pasteurization of milk robs us every year of as much Vitamin C as contained in the entire citrus crop in America.[1]

For some comparisons: *Modern Nutrition* reported in their "Open Forum on Milk" that raw milk produced superior bones and teeth in children than pasteurized milk, and that raw milk helped prevent dental problems, asthma, deafness, rheumatic fever and arthritis.[2] Also tuberculosis.

Raw milk was also proven to contribute to increased height and weight in children more so than pasteurized milk. And has also been known to prevent scurvy.[3]

An experiment on arthritis was carried out by Wulzen and Bahrs, known as the "Wulzen factor". Wulzen and Bahrs produced arthritis in guinea pigs; the pig's joints and wrists became stiff, and when laid on their sides they were unable to turn over. Raw cream or sugar-cane molasses, cured the arthritic symptoms.[4]

There are many more examples of the value of raw milk over pasteurized milk, but most people are, of course, wary of drinking raw milk because of the fear of undulant fever. However, properly nourished cows do not contract the infectious bacterial disease as readily as cows eating a deficient unbalanced diet.

Here are other findings:

"From the health standpoint, as in the case of tuberculin testing, insistence on Bang's testing of all herds producing milk, whether or not it is to be pasteurized, would solve the problem of bovine undulant fever."[5]

So if you're going to put a cow in your storage, have her tested for disease and feed her an adequate diet. Then to make sure you have clean raw milk, you must: 1. Start with clean cows with clean udders and teats. 2. Keep your utensils clean and sterilized. 3. Provide clean water for the cows to drink. 4. Allow only healthy, clean and conscientious persons to handle the milk. 5. Use small covered milk pails. 6. Refrigerate the milk at 50 degrees after milking.[6]

Dairy scientist, LeRoy Zaeske, however, cautioned that for many, many years he witnessed some of the practices of slothful milkers (before milking machines) and to this day won't lift a glass of milk to his lips unless the milk has been pasteurized.

The American Medical Association also points out that milk is more safe today than it was 30 years ago.[7]

But if you have access to clean raw milk—grab it. It's far superior to the milk now sitting on our grocery shelves. Raw milk supplies varying amounts of lipids (lecithin); complete protein; calcium; phosphorus; Vitamins A, C, D, K, E; riboflavin; niacin; thiamine; potassium; etc. But if for any reason you question the safety of raw milk, pasteurize it. (I believe that any safe milk is better than no milk at all. I'd personally buy commercial milk rather than have my family go without.)

How to Pasteurize Milk

To pasteurize any milk product use one of these four home methods:

1. Heat milk (use a candy, jelly or dairy thermometer) to 141 degrees to 145 degrees and hold at that temperature for 20 minutes. Cool quickly to avoid a cooked taste. An open kettle canner is ideal, using canning jars. Pour milk to about two inches from the top of heat-proof jars. Fill the open kettle with water just above the milk line on jars. Put the jars in the canner, and place a thermometer in one of the jars.

2. Heat milk to 161 degrees for 15 seconds. If you heat the milk over direct heat, the milk will usually scorch at this temperature. Cool quickly.

3. Use this method only in emergencies, as milk flavor will change: Add about one inch milk in a pan; bring to a fast rolling boil, stirring. Immerse pan quickly in cold water until the bottom of the pan feels cool, then refrigerate in a clean covered container.

4. Adele Davis says: "if 'pasteurization' is necessary, it can be done by the natural methods of souring or changing into yogurt."[8] (See yogurt section.)

A fishy taste in milk results if heating is done in a copper pan. A cardboard, strong or unpleasant milk flavor results if the cows aren't getting a proper diet.

How Much Milk?

Mothers should be aware of the problems involved in overconsumption of milk (moderation in all things is the answer). Pediatricians say that heavy milk drinkers may develop anemia, constipation, rickets, excessive mucuous, malnutrition, endocrine dysfunction, sleeping sickness, kidney disorders, vitamin deficiencies and excessive deposits of calcium.

So don't let your children live on milk; it robs them of too many other vital foods. Just let milk supplement the diet.

Here is a guide:

Children up to 8 years - 2 to 3 cups
Children 9 to 12 years - 3 or 4 cups
Teenagers - 4 cups
Adults - about 2 cups
Pregnant women - 3 or more cups
Nursing mothers - 4 or more cups
Senior citizens - 2 or 3 cups

Let's not forget that milk doesn't have to just come from the cup. The above allowances can be counted when any milk products are eaten.

To supply calcium, the following are alternatives for *1 cup of milk:*

1-1/3 ounces natural cheddar cheese
1-1/3 cups creamed cottage cheese
1 cup custard
1-1/3 cups ice cream. (Beware of using ice milk because of the high sugar content)
¾ cup homemade macaroni and cheese
1 milkshake (made with 2/3 cups milk and ½ cup ice cream)
1 cup oyster stew
1/5 of 15 inch-diameter round pizza, made with cheese topping
1 cup pudding (made with milk and cornstarch)
1-1/3 cup cream soup, prepared with milk
1 cup yogurt

If you eat any of the above in the course of a day, you're consuming milk.

Milk products listed from highest to lowest according to their nutritional benefits:

1. Mothers' milk
2. Yogurt from goat's milk
3. Goat's milk (some claim it's better than cow's milk but it is very difficult to find)
4. Yogurt made from clean whole raw milk (see yogurt)
5. Clean raw whole milk
6. Butter and buttermilk made from clean raw whole milk, consumed together (see butter and buttermilk).
7. Yogurt made from clean raw skim milk
8. Clean raw skim milk

9. Yogurt made from non-fat dry milk (sprayed method, see yogurt)
10. Yogurt made from pasteurized whole milk
11. Non-fat dry milk - use butter for the fat soluble vitamins
12. Pasteurized whole milk (Also probably dry whole milk)*
13. Cultured, commercial buttermilk (Commercial buttermilk might challenge pasteurized whole milk to the No. 10 spot as it has valuable lactic acid. See buttermilk)
14. Canned evaporated milk ⎤ These two are about the same.
15. Commercial skim milk ⎦
16. Canned evaporated skim milk
17. Sweetened condensed milk

Note - "Regular" non-fat dried milk is nutritionally superior and has better storage qualities than "instant" non-fat dried milk; if you have a choice use "regular"; if you have no choice "instant" is still considered a good buy.

Cream is not listed on the chart, but clean raw cream is far superior to commercial cream. (See Wulzen Factor)

Mothers - Nurse Your Babies

The most valuable milk of all is mother's milk. There is no real substitute for this highly valued life-giving food. There is no other food that gives such natural immunity to infant disease and illness. If possible, nurse your babies!

Approximate percentage composition of human milk and cow's milk:[9]

The vitamin content in human milk is superior to cow's milk. Also be aware that human milk has ten times more vitamin E than cow's milk.

	Human Milk	Cow's Milk		Human Milk	Cow's Milk
Fat	3.5	3.5	Mg	.005	.013
Sugar	7.5	4.7	K	.048	.154
Total Protein	1.25	3.4	Na	.011	.060
Lactalbumin	0.75	0.50	P	.015	.090
Casein	0.50	3.5	S	.0036	.031
Total Ash	0.20	0.75	Cl	.036	.116
Ca	.034	.122	Fe	.0001	.0004
			Cu	.00003	.00002

---

*Dry whole milk has such poor keeping qualities that I didn't give it a place of its own.

Yogurt
An Almost Perfect Food

Have you ever dreamed of finding the fountain of youth and of having more zest for life and of having a peaches and cream complexion? Cathryn Elwood in *Feel Like a Million* advises everyone that to make these dreams become realities, eat lots of yogurt.[1]

Raw milk is known to be one of the most beneficial foods available, but yogurt surpasses it in many ways.

Elwood describes how Eli Melchnikoff (Ilya Ilick Mechnikov) a 19th century Nobel prize winner who discovered the white corpuscles, was the first person to direct our attention to the yogurt-eating, long-living Bulgarians. His studies brought to our attention the 1934 census, showing us that for every million population, Bulgaria had almost 1700 vigorous, robust, healthy people over 90 years old; the United States by comparison had only nine - feeble-minded, wheel-chaired - ninety-year olds in every million.

Zesty Old Age

Bulgarian oldsters were as full of life as our 50-year olds, and Dr. Melchnikoff believed that their youth was due to the vast amounts of yogurt (made from acidophilus cultures) they consumed. Modern scientists tend to agree.

Just recently Russia exposed their long-living high-mountain families when the oldest member died. He received much publicity because he refused any medical assistance, and, it is thought, he would have lived many more years due to the physical condition of his body, if medical help had been administered. He was only 168 years old.

Many Russian families atop this mountain are decades over 100 years old and do you know what they eat daily? Lots of soured milk food.

Bacterial Warfare in Your Innards

Yogurt (a soured milk food) has the wonderful lactic acid that aids in protein, calcium and iron assimilation. It creates a friendly bacteria that attacks the harmful bacteria lurking around our innards. (If gas results from eating yogurt don't be discouraged. It's a sign that a battle is going on in your behalf. It's an indication that you are in need of this friendly bacteria assistance. The gassy feeling leaves you quickly and also makes you a little more healthy.

Yogurt, with all its other little miraculous qualities, manufactures B vitamins in the intestinal track; it also supplies the body with predigested complete protein. It is excellent in soothing indigestion (better than antacids or bicarbonate of soda), and it can also relieve constipation.

Life Saver Food

And yogurt is a marvelous natural medicine. *Modern Nutrition,* July, 1960, reports that one 8-ounce cup of yogurt has an antibiotic value equal to 14 penicillin units. The late Dr. William MacNider said, "The originator of Lactic Acid Milk has saved the lives of more children than the originator of Diptheria Antitoxin."[2]

Freshly made yogurt is more palatable than yogurt refrigerated for a few days because the acidity content of yogurt increases with storage, but the high acidity is more beneficial. Remember, however, that yogurt, except if spoiled, is beneficial regardless of when you eat it. The important thing is to make it a part of your daily eating and not just force down a bit now and then. Use it every day to realize its youth giving qualities: eat it at meal time, put it in dressings, eat it as snacks, use it in milkshakes and puddings. It is actually easy to acquire a taste for yogurt. And yogurt made from non-fat dry milk is a low-calorie food.

Easy, Healthful Food

Homemade yogurt can be more delicious and much more nutritious, can have the exact texture, but costs just a fraction of the popular commerical yogurt. Even though it's the easiest food you'll ever make, two precautions must be taken to get perfect results.

> *1. Temperature control must be maintained between 106 degrees and 120 degrees. (Heat higher or lower than this will result in failure or will give you a watery yogurt.)*
> *2. Your utensils must be absolutely clean.*

Don't let temperature control frighten you away from making this valuable food. A candy or dairy thermometer is ideal for determining proper temperature. Yogurt can also be made without a thermometer. You can learn to detect perfect yogurt temperature just by the feel of the filled yogurt jar. Yogurt temperature is just a little warmer than a baby's bottle. (However, I needed a thermometer my first few batches to get the exact yogurt-temperature feel.

Only two ingredients are necessary in making yogurt:

1. Milk - raw, pasteurized, whole, 2%, skim, non-fat dry milk, half-and-half, canned, evaporated, soy, goats milk, etc., or any of the above mixtures. [Be aware that commercial milk (not powdered or canned) can have penicillin residues and penicillin kills yogurt culture.]
2. A Yogurt Culture (Starter) - Bulgarian yogurt culture (obtainable at health food stores, claimed to be more beneficial because of the acidophilus properties); homemade or commercial yogurt; homemade yogurt cream cheese. For more effective results your "starter" should be fresh - no older than five days.

Yogurt Likes It Cozy

The important thing: you need a warm (constant) place that will keep the yogurt temperature between 106 degrees and 120 degrees for several hours. There are many good places that will keep a constant warm temperature: an electric fry pan on "warm" is best, set quart jars in the pan; a thermos bottle; a pan of warm water over a pilot light (watch it, as it can get too hot); a pan of water in a slightly warmed oven; a jar wrapped in newspaper, bedding, or in a heating pad; placed carefully by a constantly burning fire, etc. After much testing and checking, I've discovered another good yogurt bed is on top of my furnace against a hot pipe; yet my neighbor's yogurt failed miserably on top of her furnace because our furnaces weren't exactly alike. So find a perfect yogurt bed in your home. If you can't find a consistently warm place, a yogurt-maker isn't a bad investment. They cost from ten to fifteen dollars, and you can get perfect results every time. It's an investment that quickly pays for itself.

You can make yogurt in almost any container (not copper or aluminum) that is meticulously clean. Small containers give you faster results than larger ones; some yogurts incubate in three hours, some take up to 12 hours. However, be sure and refrigerate your yogurt the minute it is set, to avoid getting a tangy flavor.

Gently Does It

Yogurt is sensitive, so don't jostle it around when you test it while it's incubating. Its tender curd will "weep" and the whey will separate giving a Little Miss Muffet - curds and whey texture.

Don't be discouraged if you don't get results the first time. But try, try again! Remember constant temperature and clean utensils give results.

Every recipe I came across said to scald the milk but that isn't necessary if you're using non-fat dry milk.

Here is my simple recipe:

Non-Fay Dry Milk Yogurt

1 qt. hot tap water (120 degrees)-check with a candy or bottle thermometer if available.
Quickly stir in:
1-1/3 c. (or more) non-fat dry milk. *
Then add:
2 or 3 tablespoons yogurt culture.

Cover with a lid and cover the bottle (light destroys Vitamin B-2). A man's stocking cut in half slipped on the bottle is a perfect cover—don't tell your husband.

Put in a warm bed making sure the temperature doesn't drop below 106 degrees. If you have success, it will be ready in 3 to 12 hours. Refrigerate and eat. Remember to save 2 or 3 tablespoons for your next batch.

If yogurt doesn't set up, possibly your milk has bacteria, so boil milk first, then cool to 120° before adding culture.-

Put the jar in an open kettle on top of a wash cloth, and put water up to the milk level, then heat on top of your stove. You can hook your clean thermometer on the bottle, and when the milk registers about 110 degrees to 120 degrees, add your culture and put it to bed. (You can also just heat your milk in a pan, but the above method prevents scorching and stirring). Also, if your milk heats to over 120 degrees, just cool it to 120 degrees, add your culture, then put it tò bed. Extreme high heat (over 120 degrees) will kill your culture.

If you have access to raw milk, the yogurt it makes is unbelievably delicious. Yogurt made from any whole milk is, of course, more creamy, but it's also more fattening. Some whole milk yogurts do look curdly, but when refrigerated they go to a smooth texture. Also any yogurt failure can be reheated and started over by adding a new culture, though sometimes the reheating will turn it to cheese (see cheese).

It's The Jack-Of-All Trades

Yogurt can be used in every kind of recipe. It's delicious in drinks, milk shakes, puddings, dressings, sauces, soups, pie fillings, ice creams, sherbets, cakes, cookies, etc.,—use it in everything. Start adding yogurt to everything for remarkably improved health. Experiment and invent your own recipes.

Yogurt Variety

1. When making yogurt, sweeten the milk before heating by adding honey, molasses, or half honey and half molasses. Molasses drizzled over ready-made yogurt gives it a caramel flavor.
2. Before your yogurt is ready to put in its warm bed, add fresh liquefied fruits such as peaches, plums, apricots, apples and cinnamon, raspberries, strawberries etc. Add a little honey if extra sweetener is desired.
3. If you are a "chocolate nut," add three to five tablespoons carob flour to each quart when culture is added.
4. Don't put commercially sweetened jams, jellies or syrups into or onto your food. Make your own nutritious fruit sauce and live longer. Pour concentrated orange juice or other juices over yogurt, straight from the can and stir.

Yogurt Tips

1. Commercial yogurt should be used within ten days for freshness and high quality.

2. Homemade yogurt should be used in six or seven days for freshness - any yogurt, however, will keep for two weeks.
3. If your homemade yogurt gets harder to set after about a month, start with a fresh culture.

How to Put Yogurt in Storage

If yogurt is dried you lose the marvelous lactic acid quality, so don't bother drying it. If you store non-fat dry milk and a culture, you can always have yogurt. Yogurt is one of the most valuable foods in the world. It helps keep you well. Store lots of powdered milk just to make yogurt.

General Milk Information

Whole Milk

All Grade A milk and milk products sold today are pasteurized—heated to kill the harmful bacteria—but the process kills much of the original food value. Grade A pasteurized milk, according to the standards recommended in the Pasteurized Milk Ordinance, must come from healthy cows and may be produced, pasteurized, and handled only under strict sanitary control enforced by state and local milk sanitation officials. Requirements may vary in different localities. The "Grade A" rating designated germ-free rather than wholesomeness.

Milkfat usually constitutes about 3.25 percent of whole milk. Homogenized milk has been treated to reduce the size of the milkfat globules. In homogenized milk the cream does not separate and the product stays uniform throughout.

In vitamin D milk, the (synthetic) vitamin D content has been increased to at least 400 U.S.P. units per quart. This is the minimum daily requirement for children, pregnant women and nursing mothers.

Dry Whole Milk

Dry whole milk is pasteurized whole milk with the water removed. It has only limited retail distribution. Dry whole milk is distributed mostly to chocolate and candy manufacturers.

Because of its fat content, dry whole milk doesn't keep as well as non-fat dry milk. It is known to lose 60 percent of its vitamin A content if stored for 9 months. Also, if it is not used soon after the package is opened, it develops an off-flavor.

Commercial Lowfat Milk

Lowfat milk usually has between 0.5 and 2 percent milkfat, depending on state regulations. This kind of milk may also be labeled "2%" or "2-10" milk in the store. Lowfat milk can be "made" at home by using half whole milk and half skim or non-fat dry milk.

Commercial Skim—Blue Milk

Skim milk usually has less than 0.5 percent milkfat, the percentage recommended to states under the Pasteurized Milk Ordinance. It is often fortified with synthetic vitamins A and D, (not very generous) because the fat-soluble vitamins A, D, E and K are reduced, by the milk being sent through a clarifier and cream separator; then it is pasteurized. There is considerable loss in food value, due to both cream separation and pasteurization. The poor milk not only looks blue, it probably feels blue because it's a poor buy for your food dollar.

Skim Milk Tip

The flavor and nutritional value of skim milk can be improved by adding a teaspoonful of instant dry non-fat dry milk to each glass.

Freezing Milk or Cream

Milk may be frozen, even in bottles, but it is suggested that it should be pasteurized first (see pasteurization). Leave two or three inches headroom in your milk bottle for expansion.

Cream can be frozen, but has limited use afterwards. Thawed cream should be heated first before using in ice cream recipes; also the texture of thawed cream isn't suitable for use on cereals, etc. It can be whipped, however, and it is used effectively in frozen salads, desserts, etc.

Scalded Milk?

Scalded milk is a term carried over from the days when milk had to be taken to a high heat to free it from bacteria. Since milk bacteria is no longer that type of a problem when milk is said to be "scalded" in a recipe, it usually means the warm milk will help to "hurry-up" the recipe result. Scalded milk doesn't mean scorched milk (and pans). It just means "warm". Before heating milk it helps to rinse out your pan with cold water, to prevent scorching.

If you're using powdered milk, just mix your powered milk with warm water. This way it's not necessary to heat milk on the stove if the recipe calls for "scalded milk". (Clean pans, anyone?)

Buttermilk

Buttermilk used to be the by-product of churning raw cream into butter. That particular raw buttermilk is a nutritious food, loaded with rich water-soluble minerals, left when the fat (butter) is removed.

Commercial buttermilk, (even those labeled real-churned buttermilk) has nothing to do with making butter. Much of today's buttermilk is made from either stale pasteurized milk, or skim milk to which a commercial fermenting culture is added. Even though this buttermilk has lost much of its vital nutrients through the commercial process, it is still a beneficial food due to its lactic acid quality. It is also more quickly digested than skim milk, is a good thirst quencher, and is only half the calories of whole milk. Make your own buttermilk. It's more nutritious and economical than commercial buttermilk, (Recipe below.)

Homemade Buttermilk

1 quart room temperature milk (or 1 quart luke warm water and 1-1/3 cups powdered milk)
⅛ teaspoon salt
½ cup buttermilk

Stir well and cover. Let stand at room temperature until clabbered. Stir to smoothness. Refrigerate and drink.

Tips on Buttermilk

Always keep buttermilk chilled. If allowed to warm, it may separate. If your buttermilk should separate, just stir it.

Natural buttermilk (a by-product of butter-making) is not sold in consumer packages. It is dried and used in pancake mixes and bakery products. It is also a very valuable food.

Chocolate Milk

Commercial chocolate flavored milk is made from pasteurized whole milk with sugar and chocolate syrup or cocoa added. This milk has many additives used to thicken the milk such as alignates, carboxymethylcellulose and carrageen. In most states, regulations require, that to be labeled chocolate flavored milk, the product must be made from whole milk; to be labeled chocolate flavored milk drink, it must be made from skim or partially skimmed milk.

Strawberry or maple flavorings are sometimes used for other flavored milk and milk drinks.

"Note" - One must be aware that chocolate and cocoa interfere with calcium assimilation in the body. So if you want to do your family a favor avoid chocolate milk, cocoa, etc. in the diet (See chocolate). Indulge only occasionally.

There is a wonderful substitute for chocolate called "Carob". It has a chocolate-like flavor, is rich in vitamins and minerals, and is considered a good food. Carob may be purchased in some grocery stores, and health food stores. I'll bet all the grocery stores would start stocking it if the demand increased.

Evaporated Milk

So you'll know what you're up against in storing evaporated milk, here are some canned milk facts and storage hints, but you must remember that any milk stored is better than no milk at all.

Nutrition Review pointed out that canned evaporated milk loses half of its vitamin B-6 during the canning process, so if a baby is dependent on this *particular* milk, vitamin B-6 should be supplemented or convulsive seizures are possible.[1] Such additives as: calcium chloride, (used to preserve wood and dust unpaved roads) disodium phosphate, sodium citrate, and carrageenan chondrus extract can be present in this milk. These additives do not contribute to good health.

What's more, canned milk doesn't have good shelf life. In fact, it should be stored in a cool place like fresh milk. After two years of storage, analysis showed extensive losses of Vitamin A, riboflavin, and E. When it was stored at 100 degrees F. for this period of time, four amino acids were destroyed.[2]

So if you're storing canned milk, store it in the coolest place possible a cold refrigerator preferred, and rotate it religiously.

Evaporated milk is prepared by heating homogenized whole milk under a vacuum to remove half of its water. It is then sealed in cans and sterilized (killing most of its food value). Always refrigerate evaporated milk after opening it.

Sweetened Condensed Milk

Sweetened condensed milk is canned (condensed or evaporated) milk to which 40% refined sugar and/or refined corn syrup has been added.

Imitation Milk

There's a new product on the market called imitation milk, and that's just what it is—imitation. Would you believe that this so-called milk consists of water, corn syrup, vegetable oil (hydrogenated coconut oil), sodium caseinate, potassium phosphate, (a urinary acidifier), salt, stabilizer, emulsifier, artificial coloring and flavoring, and synthetic supplements. The ultimate in synthetics.

"Filled" milk is similar, but it contains some non-fat dry milk.

These milk manufacturers claim that their product has advantages over cow's milk, because it doesn't contain the highly saturated butterfat found in milk. That's a fact. But what they neglect to tell the public is that the milk contains coconut oil which is very highly saturated, possibly more so than the butterfat in cow's milk.

When the nutritional value of filled and imitation milks were compared to cow's milk, it was concluded that they are not a nutritional replacement for milk in proteins, minerals and vitamins.[3]

Several nutritionists stated, that the imitation milks and filled milks as formulated today are unsuitable for infants and children...from the standpoint of low protein content, essential amino acids and minerals. These imitations pose possible dangers for pregnant women, and nursing mothers, poorly nourished people and senior citizens.[4]

General Milk Hints

All milks should be tightly covered and kept at about 40 degrees. Milk will retain a high quality for three to five days.

Keep milk out of the sunlight as it destroys the valuable Vitamin B2 content.

Section IV

Non-Fat Dry Milk

Non-fat dry milk is considered one of the best buys in the grocery store, and it is a valuable storage item. "Regular non-fat dry milk is superior to "instant" non-fat dry milk."

Some nutritionists claim that non-fat dry milk stands second to raw milk in terms of nutritive value. They say it is more nutritious than commercial whole milk.[1] So don't think you're depriving your family when you serve them powdered milk in any form, it's a very valuable food. Just use butter (not margarine) for those necessary fat soluble vitamins. It should be consumed with the milk for top benefits.

Save Money - Be Your Own Milkman

Let it also be known that non-instant dry milk solids are the best protein buy in the stores. For 15 to 20 cents (at this printing) a day you can get your total protein allowance. That's pretty inexpensive protein when you compare it with steak. A family of four could also save up to $15.00 a month by using this reconstituted product rather than have commercial milk delivered to the door. Dry milk isn't recommended for baby formulas because of its high sucrose content and its lack of EFA. (Essential Fatty Acids)

Non-fat dry milk usually has less than 0.5 percent milk fat, the percentage recommended to states under the Pasteurized Milk Ordinance; and it is usually fortified with synthetic Vitamins A and D.

Since non-fat dry milk is made by removing all the fat and water from regular milk, it is good for weight watchers having approximately 80 calories per 8 ounce glass, compared to whole milk's 150 calories. That's a saving of almost half the calories.

There are two methods of commercial drying that you should be aware of to get maximum food value for your money. Here are the facts:

Drum or Roller Drying

One dry milk process, drum or roller drying, requires extremely high heat. When the milk goes over the very hot metal surfaces, the composition of milk protein is destroyed. All vitamins are reduced, and the important amino acid, lysine, is almost totally destroyed. The *Journal of Nutrition* reported that in an experiment, animals fed drum-dried milk deteriorated rapidly.

Spray Drying

Spray drying does not harm the important food values in milk. The skimmed milk is pasteurized, after butterfat is removed, and is partially evaporated. The remains are blown through nozzles into a low temperatured vacuum. The important amino acid, lysine, is not destroyed by this process.

As you can see these two drying methods give considerable contrasts in food value. The spray method keeps the milk quality high while the drum method destroys much of the milk quality due to the high heat used.

The drum roller is method is outdated and isn't being used as much. I think it would be wise however, to check your drymilk source because dry milk should be included generously in your food storage. An inferior milk could prove to be detrimental. Be aware that the label need not state the process.

Instant Verses Regular

When purchasing your powdered milk, buy "regular" rather than "instant," if you have a choice. Regular non-fat dry milk is more nutritious, not having to go through another process to be "puffed-up". Also make certain the milk you buy has "enriched" on it.

"Note"

Instant non-fat dry milk mixes easily in warm or cold water. Regular non-fat dry milk is more nutritious, but it's more difficult to mix. Use a little warm water and make a paste, then add cold water gradually stirring. It will mix well with cold water in a blender, however.

POWDERED MILK RECONSTITUTION TABLE

Use directions on package or use this reconstitution table:

Powdered Milk	Water	Cups Milk
1-1/2 Tbsp.	1/4 cup	1/4 cup
3 Tbsp.	1/2 cup	1/2 cup
4 Tbsp. (1/4 c.)	3/4 cup	3/4 cup
6 Tbsp. (1/3 c.)	1 cup	1 cup
8 Tbsp. (1/2 c.)	1-1/2 cups	1-1/2 cups
1 cup	3 cups	3 cups
1-1/3 cups	1 quart	1 quart
2-2/3 cups	1/2 gallon	1/2 gallon

Non-Fat Dry Milk Storage Hints

Instant non-fat dry milk will store up to one and one-half years in a cool dry place. Regular has better storing qualities; it will keep up to two and one-half years in a cool, dry place. Some manufacturer's claim longer storage but invariably it goes stale after about thirty months, if kept in a bag. Vacuum sealed in a can has long term storage.

After your dry milk is opened for use, be careful to keep the bag sealed tightly and continue to keep it in a cool dry place. Bacteria can grow if moisture enters an opened package of powdered milk. After milk is reconstituted treat it as fresh milk.

Don't forget that almost all foods lose value the longer they are stored. It is wise to rotate always.

Powdered "whole" milk doesn't store well because of the fat content. Dr. Henry Barssook, author of *Vitamins* points out that powdered "whole" milk loses about 60 percent of it's vitamin A content when stored for 9 months.

Non-Fat Dry Milk Hints

1. When milk needs to be heated, heat your water; remove from heat (so it won't boil over) then add your dry milk. This method prevents scorching and tedious stirring.
2. To have a continuous cold container of milk (and cold milk is the secret of good reconstituted milk), always keep a cold jug of water in the refrigerator to use for making quick cold milk.
3. Dry reconstituted milk scorches more easily than other milks so always use very low heat or double boilers.

4. To avoid lumpy sauces using dry milk, use only the recommended proportions (6 tablespoons dry milk to 1 cup water). First combine dry milk, flour and fat, then add warm (not hot) liquid gradually. Add additional heat gradually, stirring.

5. To make powdered milk more palatable, some people add a little sweetener - 1 tbs. honey or sugar.

6. If your family prefers whole milk, mix half whole and half powdered reconstituted milk. You can hardly tell the difference.

7. Powdered milk added to recipes is a natural sweetner, so in using it, you may reduce the sweetening requirement called for in the recipe.

8. Add additional powdered milk to any food for a high quality addition of protein and general nutrition. A half cup of powdered milk added to a quart of any milk increases the milk's protein by 62 percent.

9. Powdered milk can be used in any recipe calling for milk. Add the milk or add the powder and water.

Bonus Uses of Powdered Milk:

Yogurt, cream cheese, hard cheese, cottage cheese, buttermilk, etc. (See index for pages)

The Exposure of Cheeses

I honestly regretted putting the factual information about commercial cheddar cheeses into this book because cheddar cheeses cannot be made inexpensively at home unless you have a cow (moo hoo). It takes, actually, one-half gallon of whole milk to make one-half pound of cheddar cheese. So, you can see it's cheaper to buy your hard cheeses at the local market. But here's the local market problem:

Bleach In My Cheese?

Fifteen years ago the National Cheese Institute filed a petition with the Federal Drug Administration seeking permission to add hydrogen peroxide to milk in manufacturing cheddar-type cheeses. The hydrogen peroxide kills the bacteria and bleaches the cheese, and also destroys the valuable Vitamin A. A catalase is then added to the product to remove the hydrogen peroxide.

There were many heated objections concerning this petition because the harmful bleach would certainly camouflage lower quality and inferior cheeses, would mask unsanitary milk practices, and would definitely cripple the nutritive value of this valuable food.

Despite these objections, the Federal Drug Administration ruled in favor of using bleaches in cheese making. So you'll be as discouraged as I was to find that cheeses are bleached with calcium sulfate (plaster of paris—mixed with flour, it is used to kill rodents), magnesium carbonate, benzoyl peroxide, or with potassium alum mixed with benzoyl peroxide.

They tell us we are protected by labeling, but the majority of cheese is cut from large wedges (that hold the original labels), so we get no labels and no information. Ignorance, in the case of cheese is bliss, I guess.

All This and Pesticides Too

As with milk and butter, some cheese is contaminated with pesticide residues. And contamination is a bigger problem than we realize. The residue of pesticides is allowed to be 0.3 ppm, but spot checks found pesticide residues in many cases to be much higher than the allowance and were considered harmful. It makes one wonder what the cheeses contain, that are never checked by the inspectors. I think we, the consumer, had better start complaining to the cheese manufacturers.

The Betsy Solution

For those of you who are lucky enough to have "old Betsy" grazing in your alfalfa patch, giving you ample milk, here is a marvelous cheddar cheese recipe, that absolutely duplicates (and surpasses) commercial hard cheese.

Before you begin making cheese, let me remind you that all cheese is naturally white. (Have you ever seen a cow that gives orange milk?). Seriously, even the cheese manufacturers aren't magic, so the cheese that isn't white usually has had food coloring added to it. If you must have orange cheese, add the coloring before pasteurizing the milk. (If you prefer polka-dotted cheese add the coloring after the cheese curd is formed.)

For delicious cheese, remember that cheese can be no better than the milk it's made from.

Homemade Cheddar Cheese
Yield - 1 pound cheddar cheese

1 gallon whole milk
½ cup cultured buttermilk
yellow food coloring, if desired
add salt to taste later.

All utensils must be sanitary in making cheese (unsanitary utensils break down the yeast molds), so clean everything used in cheese-making in a 50 percent Clorox solution (1 cup Clorox to 1 cup water). Most cheese makers recommend pasteurizing milk for this reason.

Put milk and buttermilk into your clean container and heat to 80 degrees F. Maintain this temperature for 12 or more hours, or until curd is formed. (See yogurt section for maintaining a warm temperature.)

Pour formed curds (they won't be pretty) into a clean cheese cloth, and rinse gently with cool water. Put salted clean water (no salt, if desired) and curds into a pan and heat very slowly until cheese forms a ball. You can eat as is, or soak cheese ball in a salt brine (6 tablespoons salt to 1 quart of water) for 48 hours. Store in an air tight container or plastic bag.

You can cure cheese, if desired, by wrapping cheese in a cheese cloth, dipping it in melted wax, and leaving in a 50 degree temperature (your refrigerator, or a 50 degree area) for 30 days or longer—six weeks is preferred aging period.

This cheese can be used in any way or recipe using commercial cheddar cheese.

For two economical cheese recipes, see Homemade Process Cheese and Skim Milk Cheese.

Cheese Cookery

Successful cheese cookery depends on brief heating at a low temperature. High temperatures and long cooking make cheese tough and stringy and cause the fat to separate out. Also, some of the flavor is lost.

Cheese blends more readily with other ingredients and melts more quickly if you shred or dice it first. One-half pound of cheese yields about 2 cups of shredded cheese.

Soft, well-aged Cheddar melts and blends with other ingredients more readily than less-ripened cheese, and less Cheddar is needed because it has a more pronounced flavor. Processed cheese also melts and blends readily but has a much milder flavor. (See processed cheese.)

Melt cheese in the top of a double boiler over simmering water or add it to a hot mixture. When making cheese sauce, stir shredded cheese into the completed white sauce and heat only enough to melt the cheese. When making a cheese omelet, add the shredded cheese after the omelet is cooked, just before folding.

Cheese can be melted under the broiler, too. Open-face cheese sandwiches can be made this way. Place the sandwich so the cheese is 4 or 5 inches from the heat. Broil just until the cheese begins to melt.

Casserole dishes containing cheese should be baked at low to moderate temperatures. To prevent cheese toppings from toughening or hardening during baking, cover them with foil or crumbs or add the cheese just a few minutes before removing the food from the oven.

To Make Skim Milk Cheeses
(Basic Hints)

1. The only ingredients necessary to make skim milk cheeses are dry powdered milk, water and something that will curdle the milk (see below).

2. Skim milk cheeses are very easy to make. (Tell somebody "I Love You" twenty-four times and presto, it's done—takes about one minute.)

3. Don't use whole milk in making skim milk cheese, as the cream just goes into the whey, leaving a skim milk curd.

4. Avoid using a highly concentrated, reconstituted milk because it's too difficult to curdle. Use the regular recipe (1-1/3 cups powdered milk to 1 quart of water) for best results.

5. In making skim milk cheeses, take note that to get a hard skim milk cheese use low temperatures in heating your milk. To get a softer cheese, use high (almost boiling) temperatures. The high temperature breaks up the curd. (See recipes.)

6. Cheeses you make will have no preservatives so they are highly perishable. Use them within three or four days.

7. Skim milk cheeses will not melt when heated because there's no fat content. If you desire the melting qualities, but want to stretch your cheese dollar, grate half Cheddar cheese and half skim milk cheese and mix together. For an economical cheese that will melt, see "Homemade Process Cheese".

8. Don't dismiss skim milk cheeses as not being a versatile food just because they won't melt. Grated or chopped hard skim milk cheese makes a delicious sandwich spread, is good in casseroles, or in tossed or molded salads and is fun to dip in fondue sauce, etc. Soft, skim milk cheese (blended until

smooth) can be used like cream cheese. It's a very nutritious food, so let your imagination get some exercise (your bodies too, if you haven't passed the body energy crisis).

9. For more calories and more flavor, add a little melted butter to the skim milk cheese curd, after the curd is formed.

10. Skim milk cheeses are very low caloried so use them generously in your diet.

What Curdles Milk?

(Add to warm or hot milk any of the following - see recipes.)

1. Sprinkle a few grains of Ascorbic Acid powder over milk - purchase at drug or health food stores.

2. Dissolve 3 or 4 Rennet (Junket) tablets in a little cold water before adding to milk - purchase at grocery, drug or health food stores.

3. Add a tablespoon at a time of lemon juice or any highly acid fruit juices.

4. Dissolve 4 or 5 (or more) crushed vitamin C pills in a little cold water.

5. Add several tablespoons of any soured milk products - clabbered raw milk, homemade yogurt cream cheese, etc.

6. Add a teaspoon at a time of vinegar - leaves a slight vinegar taste.

7. Add several tablespoons honey or molasses - leaves a very sweet taste.

8. Salt is known to be a curdler of milk but the amount necessary to curdle it, makes the cheese unpalatable.

You can use smaller amounts of any one of the above milk curdlers and put over very low heat, stirring periodically, and the milk will slowly curdle - for fast results just use the suggested amounts above (or more).

Hard Skim Milk Cheese (Low Calorie)

1 quart milk makes about 1 cup cheese (4 ounces)
1 quart skim milk (1-1/3 cups powdered milk and 1 quart warm water)

A cheese curdler - The milk curdler can be ascorbic acid or 4 or more tablespoons lemon juice of other highly acid fruit, or several tablespoons soured milk product (see What Curdles Milk?).

Put warm milk in a pan and add milk curdler. Heat very slowly on a very low heat. Cheese will form a ball. Put cheese ball in the piece of cheese cloth and squeeze out liquid or just squeeze out liquid with clean hands. Eat as is, or chill in a well covered bowl.

Tangy Hard Skim Milk Cheese (Low Calorie)

(Don't use whole milk as the cream goes into the whey.)

Put homemade skim milk yogurt, buttermilk, clabbered raw milk or any sour-milk product in a pan and warm gently over low heat. Cheese will form, so gently stir into a ball. Squeeze out water from the cheese ball and eat, or refrigerate in a well covered container.

Cheese Nuts

Grind skim milk cheese. Let dry and use as chewy nuts in any recipe.

Making Soft Cheeses

No more need be said (nag, nag) about some of the unhealthy additives put in commercial dairy products. Let's just emphasize that it is better for your health if you are able to make your own. Soft cheeses are very easy to make in your home, but remember that they are highly perishable because no preservatives are added. You should use them within three or four days. Here are some general hints and recipes:

Hints for Making Soft Cheeses

1. Cream cheese made from yogurt has a good tangy flavor. If your cheese is too tart, add one or more teaspoons salad dressing or add any of your food powders, or add 1 or 2 tablespoons butter with seasoning to mask tanginess.
2. If the cheese bag is dry, the cheese has hung too long and it will be dry and crumbly (see dry curds recipes). Cream cheese is ready when cheese is moist and bag is still damp.
3. Be aware of the cloth or bag that you're putting your cream cheese in, as the cheese will pick up the flavor the cloth. I bleached my cloths and my cheese tasted like Clorox.
4. Always catch and use the whey that drips from your cheese bag. Use it in your cooking as it is a very valuable food (see whey).

5. It takes ¾ quart yogurt or clabbered raw milk to make 1 cup cream cheese—1½ quarts = 2 cups.

6. One cup (8 ounces) homemade cream cheese costs less than half the price of commercial cream cheese.

Cream Cheese (not tangy)

Bring whole milk almost to a boil (don't scorch). Add several tablespoons yogurt and whey (or any other milk curdler - see milk curdlers). Pour formed curds into a cheese cloth bag. Remove and immediately refrigerate or hang for 3 to 4 hours or until you have moist cream cheese - don't over-dry. (If curds are crumbly, add a tiny bit of milk or cream and beat well in a blender or mixer.) This is almost an exact duplicate for commercial cream cheese. Let me remind you, if you try to use skim milk for this recipe it will turn into hard skim milk cheese. (See hard skim milk cheeses.) (If you over-dry curds, add a little cream for quick cottage cheese.)

Tangy Low Calorie Cream Cheese

¾ quart yogurt = 1 cup (8 ounces) cream cheese

Put a square piece of cheese cloth (or a piece of an old clean sheet) over a strainer or colander. And set the strainer in a large bowl. Pour homemade or commercial yogurt into the cloth. Pick up the four corners of the cloth (making a bag) and hang it over the bowl. Let it hang from 18 to 24 hours (if the bag dries out - it has hung too long).

Presto—Low Calorie Cream Cheese.

No Effort Yogurt Cheese

Set milk with an added yogurt culture (like you are making yogurt) in a very warm (110 degrees) place for about 24 hours. Cheese curd will go to the bottom with the whey on top. (Heat gently if a firmer cheese curd is desired.) Remove curd, then squeeze out excess moisture, and refrigerate in an air-tight container.

Soft Skim Milk Cheese

(Also quick cottage cheese)

Use Hard Skim Milk Cheese recipe, but instead bring 1 quart water to a rapid; boil, take off heat and add powdered milk stirring, (you can bring 1 quart skim milk to a boil, but the above method prevents the milk from scorching), then add culture. (The high heat breaks up the curd making a softer curd - almost like cream cheese.) For a smooth cream cheese, mash fine or put in a blender. Dry the loose curd (hang in a cheese cloth bag) and add a little cream for a quick cottage cheese.

Tangy Rich Cream Cheese

Follow above recipe but make your yogurt out of whole milk. For extra, extra rich cream cheese, use yogurt made from half and half.

Farmer's Cheese

Extremely white cheese.

Merely follow the recipe for Tangy Low Calorie Cream Cheese, but use firm clabbered raw milk instead of yogurt. Almost an exact duplicate for commercial sour cream.

Skimmed-Off-the-Top Cheese

The skim on slowly heated milk, taken off and put in a bag, makes a cheese. When enough skim has been removed to make a small ball of cheese, just squeeze out excess liquid, and refrigerate in an air-tight container.

Flavored Cream Cheese

Add any flavors to the milk before making into yogurt or before curdling to get flavored cream cheese. Also pour the flavored whey into ice cube trays for popsicles or flavored cubes for drinks.

Cream Cheese on Potatoes

Any of your homemade cream cheeses with a little seasoning salt added, are delicious on baked potatoes. It tastes just like sour cream, and is so low caloried, it can help to take the wiggle out of your walk.

Cream Cheese Chip Dippity Dip

Add a little milk to your cream cheese and stir until smooth. Add any food powders, mushrooms, fruits, etc. for delicious low calorie chip or cracker dips. If your cream cheese is tangy, add 1 tablespoon softened butter and salt and pepper.

Cream of Celery Sticks

Use recipe for chip dips, and use to stuff celery. A delicious low calorie snack.

Pretend Deviled Eggs

Blend homemade cream cheese and salt and pepper. Tastes just like deviled egg centers. Add salad dressing and a little mustard if you wish - a good sandwich or celery filler, and is also good on small crackers.

Another Soft Cheese
Homemade Ricotta Cheese

1 13-ounce can evaporated milk
1 gallon whole milk
¼ rennet tablet (available at a drug or grocery store)

When cooking use heavy pan and cook on simmer. Heat the milk to scalding. Cool to luke warm. Put ¼ rennet tablet in ¼ cup cold water. Dissolve. Put in cooled milk. Stir. Let sit for about 4 hours in a cool place (not refrigerator) until it begins to separate. Put back on stove at low temperature until cheese and whey separate (about 30-60 minutes) until soft but holds together. Don't overcook cheese or it will become rubbery.

Put in colander that has been covered with cheese cloth. Makes 4 cups of cheese. Keeps well for about 2 weeks.

Whey - Never Throw it Away

What is whey? Whey is the milky liquid left from making cheese and is a very valuable food. Whey is 70 percent moisture, 4 percent fat, 19 percent protein, 4 percent lactose and 3 percent ash. Whey is a very good source of water-soluble vitamins and minerals, and has the spectacular vitamin B-12. In cheese making many of the B vitamins are lost into the whey so the whey is in many ways more valuable than the cheese for nutritious eating and drinking.

Use whey in your cooking, your juices, your drinks, and in all your baking especially in making bread, cookies, etc. Give it to the dog rather than throw it out or toss it on your plants, garden spot or lawn.

Whey - Hey! - Never throw it away.

Processed Cheese - The Artificial Cow

The cheese you buy in that oblong carton is about as much good as the carton.

The clever manufacturers take one-third water, one-third gelatin, one-third (any low grade) cheese, and fill it with so many emulsifiers that it cannot really be classified as food. Then they put it on the grocery store shelf for us to eat.

Triple the price of the carton and that's what you're actually paying for the cheese inside. The rest is water, gelatin, emulsifiers, chemicals and other additives.

Federal standards say this cheese is "prepared by comminuting (grinding) and mixing with the aid of heat, one or more cheeses of the same or two or more varieties...with an emulsifying agent...into a homogenous plastic mass. One or more of the optional ingredients...may be used."[1] (Isn't that reassuring)

Forty years ago, this method of making processed cheese was developed and it has never been improved. F. J. Schlink wrote in 1935 that "One of the major atrocities of this age is the disappearance of natural cheese and the substitution for it of what is called process cheese, made by grinding cheese of very low quality or any quantity that happens to be available and mixing in chemicals and emulsifiers."[2]

Beat Them at Their Own Game

Do you buy this cheese in a carton, because it's less expensive. Don't! Make your own, it's so simple, so inexpensive, and so much fun. This is one cheese you can really experiment with.

Below is the basic recipe, but you can add anything to this cheese. You can add as much or as little cheese to the basic recipe depending on the cheese taste you desire. You can stretch it as far as you want, adding more milk, more gelatin and more seasoning. My cluttered kitchen and I really had a delightful time developing this recipe. After the basic recipe emerged, then we really went wild adding pimento, mushrooms, sliced olives, chopped meat, reconstituted soy meat granules, vegetables, fruits, etc., with favorable results every time.

This cheese is very low in calories and cholesterol, and what's so great about it, is that it will melt when heated. So slice it for sandwiches, chop it or grate for salads, and melt it on your casseroles. It is really a versatile food, depending on what you add to it or how you use it.

Experiment with this fun cheese. But in doing so, let me remind you that one package of unflavored gelatin must be added for every cup of liquid or it won't be firm enough to slice. And the more cheese you add, the more cheesy taste. Also be generous with your seasonings. The seasoning makes it. So have fun with it. I certainly did.

Homemade Processed Cheese

(Basic Recipe - 4 ounces cheddar cheese = 20 ounces Process Cheese)

4 ounces (or more) cubed cheese
2 packages unflavored gelatin softened in 1 cup cold water
1 cup milk (or 1 cup water and 1/3 cup powdered milk)
Season generously to taste (garlic, onion, or seasoning powders, or almost any seasoning works well)
Yellow food coloring if you must.

Sprinkle gelatin over cold water; don't stir. Let sit ten minutes in cold water, then heat softened gelatin until dissolved. Add all ingredients in blender, and blend until smooth. Put in an oiled mold and chill until firm. Unmold. Ready to eat.

This is a bland cheese so season generously. Also, you can add pimento, sliced olives, mushrooms, meats, vegetables, fruits, etc., and blend to make a smooth flavorful cheese, or you can add them after the blending, for a chunky-filled cheese.

Use this cheese in any recipe calling for Processed Cheese.

CHEESE BUYERS GUIDE

Kind	Characteristics	Uses
Bel Paese (Bel Pah-A-say.)	Mild, sweet flavor; light, creamy-yellow interior; slate-gray surface; soft to medium-firm, creamy texture.	Appetizers, sandwiches, desserts, and snacks.
Blue	Tangy, piquant flavor; semisoft, pasty, sometimes crumbly texture; white interior marbled or streaked with blue veins of mold, resembles Roquefort.	Appetizers, salads and salad dressings, desserts, and snacks.

Brick	Mild to moderately sharp flavor; semisoft to medium-firm, elastic texture; creamy white to yellow interior; brownish exterior.	Appetizers, sandwiches, desserts, and snacks.
Brie (Bree.)	Mild to pungent flavor; soft, smooth texture; creamy-yellow interior; edible thin brown and white crust.	Appetizers, sandwiches, desserts, and snacks.
Caciocavallo (Ca-cheo-ca-vallo.)	Piquant, somewhat salty flavor— similar to Provolone, but not smoked. smooth, very firm texture; light or white interior; clay-colored or tan surface.	Snacks and desserts. Suitable for grating and cooking when fully cured.
Camembert	Distinctive mild to tangy flavor; soft, smooth texture—almost fluid when fully ripened; creamy-yellow interior; edible thin white or gray--white crust.	Appetizers, desserts, and snacks.
Cheddar (often called American.)	Mild to very sharp flavor; smooth texture, firm to crumbly; light cream to orange.	Appetizers, main dishes, sauces, soups, sandwiches, salads, desserts, and snacks.
Colby	Mild to mellow flavor, similar to Cheddar; softer body and more open texture than Cheddar; light cream to orange.	Sandwiches and snacks.
Cottage	Mild, slightly acid flavor; soft, open texture with tender curds of varying size; white to creamy white.	Appetizers, salads, used in some cheesecakes.
Cream	Delicate, slightly acid flavor; soft, smooth texture; white.	Appetizers, salads, sandwiches, desserts, and snacks.
Edam	Mellow, nutlike, sometimes salty flavor, rather firm, rubbery texture; creamy-yellow or medium yellow--orange interior; surface coated with red wax; usually shaped like a flat-tened ball.	Appetizers, salads, sandwiches, sauces, desserts, and snacks.

Gjetost (YET-ost.)	Sweetish, caramel flavor; firm, buttery consistency; golden brown.	Desserts and snacks.
Gorgonzola (Gor-gon-zo-la.)	Tangy, rich, spicy flavor; semisoft, pasty, sometimes crumbly texture; creamy-white interior, mottled or streaked with blue-green veins of mold; clay-colored surface.	Appetizers, salads, desserts and snacks.
Gouda (GOO-da.)	Mellow, nutlike, often slightly acid flavor; semisoft to firm, smooth texture, often containing small holes; creamy-yellow or medium yellow--orange interior; usually has red wax coating; usually shaped like a flattened ball.	Appetizers, salads, sandwiches, sauces, desserts, and snacks.
Gruyere (Grew-YARE.)	Nutlike, salty flavor, similar to Swiss, but sharper; firm, smooth texture with small holes or eyes; light yellow.	Appetizers, desserts, and snacks.
Liederkranz (Lee-der-krontz.)	Robust flavor, similar to very mild Limburger; soft, smooth texture, creamy-yellow interior; russet surface.	Appetizers, desserts, and snacks.
Limburger	Highly pungent, very strong flavor and aroma; soft smooth texture that usually contains small irregular openings; creamy-white interior; reddish-yellow surface.	Appetizers, desserts and snacks.
Monterey (Jack)	Semisoft; smooth, open texture, mild flavor; Cheddar-like. Hard when aged.	Appetizers, sandwiches, desserts, and snacks. Aged cheese can be grated.
Mozzarella (also called Scamorza) (Mottza-rel-la.)	Delicate, mild flavor, slightly firm, plastic texture; creamy white.	Main dishes such as pizza or lasagna, sandwiches, snacks.
Muenster (Mun-stir.)	Mild to mellow flavor; semisoft texture with numerous small openings; creamy-white interior; yellowish-tan surface.	Appetizers, sandwiches, desserts and snacks.
Mysost (Mews-ost.)	Sweetish, caramel flavor; firm, buttery consistency; light brown.	Desserts and snacks.

Neufchatel (New-sha-tel.)	Mild, acid flavor; soft, smooth texture similar to cream cheese but lower in fat; white.	Salads, sandwiches, desserts, and snacks.
Parmesan	Sharp, distinctive flavor, very hard, granular texture; yellowish white.	Grated for seasoning.
Port du Salut	Mellow to robust flavor similar to Gouda; semi-soft, smooth elastic texture; creamy white or yellow.	Appetizers, desserts, and snacks.
Provolone (Pro-vo-lo-na.)	Mellow to sharp flavor, smokey and salty; firm, smooth texture; cuts without crumbling; light creamy yellow; light-brown or golden-yellow surface.	Appetizers, main dishes, sandwiches, desserts, and snacks.
Ricotta	Mild, sweet, nutlike flavor; soft, moist texture with loose curds (fresh Ricotta) or dry and suitable for grating; white.	Salads, main dishes such as lasagna and ravioli, and desserts.
Romano	Very sharp, piquant flavor; very hard, granular texture; yellowish-white interior; greenish-black surface.	Seasoning and general table use; when cured a year it is suitable for grating.
Roquefort	Sharp, peppery, piquant flavor; semisoft, pasty, sometimes crumbly texture; white interior streaked with blue-green veins of mold.	Appetizers, salads and salad dressings, desserts, and snacks.
Sap Sago	Sharp, pungent, cloverlike flavor; very hard texture suitable for grating; light green or sage green.	Grated for seasoning.
Stilton	Piquant flavor, milder than Gorgonzola or Roquefort; open, flaky texture; creamy-white interior streaked with blue-green veins of mold; wrinkled, melon-like rind.	Appetizers, salads, desserts, and snacks.
Swiss (also called Emmentaler.)	Mild, sweet, nutlike flavor; firm, smooth, elastic body with large round eyes; light yellow.	Sandwiches, salads, and snacks.

Storing Cheese

Cheese keeps best in the refrigerator. How long it will keep depends on the kind of cheese and wrapping. Soft cheeses - such as cottage, cream, and Neufchatel— are highly perishable. Hard cheeses - such as Cheddar and Swiss—keep much longer than soft cheeses if protected from drying out.

Another method for short term cheese preservation is to wrap cheeses in clothes that have been wrung out in vinegar.

Leave cheese in its original wrapper if buying commercial cheese. Wrap homemade cheese extremely well, when refrigerating. Cover cut surfaces tightly with waxed paper, foil, or plastic to protect the surface from drying out or store the cheese in a tightly covered container (glass or enamel is best). If you want to store a large piece of cheese for an extended time, dip the cut surface in melted paraffin. Store cheese that has a strong odor (such as Limburger) in a tightly covered container. Any surface mold that develops on hard natural cheese should be trimmed off completely before the cheese is used. If this mold *penetrates* the interior of cheeses that are not ripened by molds (such as Cheddar and Swiss), cut away the moldy portions or discard the cheeses.However, in naturally mold-ripened cheeses such as Blue and Roquefort, mold is an important part of the cheese and can be eaten. Cheese that has dried out and become hard may be grated and stored in a tightly covered jar.

To Freeze Cheese

To freeze cheese, cut it in small pieces (one pound or less, not more than 1 inch thick). Wrap cheeses tightly, freeze quickly at 0 degrees F. or below, and store up to 6 months. You can use frozen cheese immediately (if your hands can with stand the strain) by grating it. Many sources suggest that you should thaw frozen cheese slowly in the refrigerator but the results are crumby, I mean crumbly—cheese. For uncrumbly cheese, let it thaw at room temperature for 24 hours, then you get good old rubbery results.

Storage Guides for Cheese

Cottage, fresh Ricotta - Refrigerate covered; use within 3 to 5 days.

Cream, Neufchatel, other soft varieties - Refrigerate covered or tightly wrapped; use within two weeks.

Cheddar, Swiss, other hard varieties - Refrigerate tightly wrapped; will keep for several months. If mold appears on the surface, just quickly cut it off, so it won't alter the cheese taste. The cheese (not the mold) is safe to eat, however.

Cheese spreads and cheese foods - Store unopened jars at room temperature; after opening, refrigerate tightly covered; store boxed or wrapped cheese food in the refrigerator; will keep for several weeks.

Cottage Cheese

Cottage cheese is a soft unripened natural cheese that can be purchased in cup-shaped containers or tumblers. It may be purchased plain or creamed and in different curd sizes. Federal standards require that it have no more than 80 percent moisture. Creamed cottage cheese contains a minimum of four percent fat content. Commercial cottage cheese should be used within three to five days.

Commercial cottage cheese may have many unhealthy additives. Sodium hypochlorite may be used in washing the curd. (Sodium hypochlorite is also used as a medical antiseptic for wounds, and is a dangerous ingested ingredient, not fit for human consumption.) Hydrogen peroxide may be used as a preservative. Diacetyl may give the butter flavor, and annatto or cochineal (used in diagnostic solutions) may be used as dyes. Many other questionable ingredients may be added to cottage cheese but don't dismiss it as being a valuable food because it can be made easily right at home. The homemade cottage cheeses are highly perishable because no preservatives are added, and should be used within three to four days.

Make Cottage Cheese in Your Cottage

Homemade cottage cheese is a tasty, nutritious (containing 20 percent milk solids), easily digested, and low-calorie food. Eat it plain or add some seasoning; eat it with vegetables or fruits, as a main dish or a dessert.

Ingredients

Milk

Milk that has been refrigerated even for a short period of time can develop undesirable bacteria resulting in off-flavor or odors in the cheese made from the milk. Cottage cheese should always be made from skim milk because the cream won't stay in the curd; it just goes into the whey. If raw milk is being used, let the milk stand a few hours, and then skim off the cream that rises to the surface. One gallon of skim milk will make about one pound of cottage cheese.

Cottage Cheese Starters

You must have a starter to get the cheese-forming process underway. The starter may be either a commercially produced lactic culture,[1] or a very fresh cultured buttermilk, (commercial buttermilk is superior to homemade buttermilk as a starter for cottage cheese but homemade buttermilk will work), or rennet.

Rennet

Use rennet if you desire a large curd cottage cheese. Rennet is available either in tablet form (junket tablets) or as an extract. You can sometimes buy tablets in drug or grocery stores; the extract is available only from rennet companies.[1]

Salt

Salt improves the flavor and keeping quality of cottage cheese, or you may use food powders.

Cream

Adding cream to cottage cheese makes a smoother and more flavorful product.

Equipment

Equipment necessary for making cottage cheese is:

1. A six to eight quart container. It is recommended that stainless steel, enamel, glass or crock type vessels are used to activate the curd. Do not use any kind of galvanized metal or aluminum container.

2. A somewhat larger container, to serve as the bottom part of an improvised double boiler for heating water. A large galvanized pail, or dishpan will do.

3. A thermometer that measures temperatures between 75 and 175 degrees F. The floating, dairy-type is best, though a candy or jelly thermometer is acceptable.

4. A long-handled spoon or stirrer that reaches to the bottom of the eight-quart container.

5. A measuring cup.

6. Measuring spoons.

7. A knife with a blade long enough to reach to the bottom of the eight quart container.

8. Cheesecloth - 18 inches square.

9. A colander and a pan large enough to hold the colander.

10. A mixing bowl made of anything but aluminum or galvanized metal (a metal with a zinc coating).

11. A covered container for storing cheese in refrigerator. Note - Making cottage cheese might seem difficult, but after the first batch it's easy.

Cottage Cheese

(Yield about 1 pound cottage cheese)

1 gallon luke warm water (about 70 degrees)
5-1/3 cups powdered milk or use pasteurized raw skim milk (they recommend pasteurization in case of foreign bacteria.
½ cup fresh cultured buttermilk

Let set in a warm 70 to 75 degrees temperature for 16 to 24 hours, or until clabbered. Cube the curd (see illustration). Let the cube rest for 10 minutes, to allow the curd to separate from the whey. Add:
2 quarts (98 to 100 degrees) water

Set the pan on a rack in a larger pan of water and heat slowly (this is the critical step in making cottage cheese), raising the temperature of the curds and whey to 100 degrees. This temperature increase takes 30 to 40 minutes—about one degree increase per minute.

During heating, stir the curd gently with a large spoon. Stir for about a minute, at five minute intervals. (This helps the curd to be heated uniformly, and prevents the curd from sticking together.)

When the curd and whey reaches 100 degrees, heat it faster and stir it more frequently. The temperature should reach 115 degrees in 10 to 15 minutes, or until the pieces are firm and don't break easily when squeezed. If the curd isn't firm enough, heat it to 125 degrees.

When the curd is firm, stop the heating process, and dip out the whey with a cup.

Pour the remaining curds and whey into a cheesecloth over a colander that you've set into another pan. Let the curd drain for two or three minutes. Don't let the curds drain too long or the curds will stick together.

Gather the corners of the cheesecloth together, with the curd, and immerse the bag in a pan of clean cold water. Raise and lower the bag several times.

Rinse the curd again in ice water to chill the curd. When the curd stops dripping, it's done.

Unseasoned cottage cheese has a definite acid flavor, so add a little seasoning if desired.

Seasoning Cottage Cheese (See Salt)

Put cottage cheese in a mixing bowl; if you're adding salt or food powder add ½ teaspoon of salt (or food powder) for each cup of curd or 1 teaspoon for each pound. Mix thoroughly.

Creaming the Curd

For every 2 cups of curd, add 5 or 6 tablespoons of either sweet or sour cream or half and half. Mix thoroughly.

Note—Skim milk may be added to the curd and seasoned, for dieters.

Large Curd Cottage Cheese

Large curd cottage cheese is made in roughly the same way as the small curd. However, besides using the basic ingredients, milk and a starter, you must also use rennet. (Follow the manufacturer's directions for using rennet, or dissolve ¼ rennet tablet in 2 tablespoons of clean, cool water. Add 1 tablespoon of rennet solution for each gallon of skim milk that you're making into cheese.)

No. 1—Warming skim milk in an improvised double boiler.

No. 2—Curd is ready to be cut when it pulls quickly and smoothly away from the side of the container.

Positions of Knife in Cutting the Curd

TOP VIEW

Step 1   Step 2

No. 3—Make perpendicular cuts from (1) back to front and (2) left to right.

SIDE VIEW   (Cross-section)

Step 3   Step 4

Follow cuts of step 1 as nearly as possible holding knife at angle shown above.

No. 4—Heating the cut curd.

No. 5—Dipping off whey.

No. 6—Draining off the last of the whey. Curd is placed in a cheese-cloth "bag," and set in a colander.

No. 7—Rinsing the curd, in a cheese-cloth "bag," by dipping it into cool water.

Easy Cottage Cheese

A suitable cottage cheese can be made by letting your cream cheese bags hang until they are almost dry. Then add a little milk or cream, and seasoning.

Pretend (Easy) Cottage Cheese

Put two quarts homemade yogurt in a cloth bag and let hang and drip until curd is quite dry (usually 24 to 26 hours). Stir in seasoning and cream. Chill in a covered bowl.

Low Calorie Sour Cream

Commercial or homemade cottage cheese can be put in a blender to make low calorie sour cream, chip dip or salad dressing. Season to taste.

Poor Cottage Cheese? Try Again

Sour acid flavor - means that too much acid developed before and during cooking of the curd, that too much whey was retained in curd, or that the curd was not sufficiently washed and drained.

Yeasty, sweet or unclean flavors - indicates that yeasts, molds, or bacteria were introduced into your cheese by unclean utensils or an impure starter; or that you milk was not pasteurized.

Soft wet curd - results from too much moisture in the cheese, the development of too much acid during cutting of the curd, heating the cut curd at too high or too low a temperature or allowing too-large curd particles to form.

Tough dry curd - results from insufficient acid development in the curd before it is cut, too fine a cutting of the curd, too high a heating temperature, or too long a holding time after cooking and before dipping off whey.

That Yummy, Yummy Cream

Raw cream is truly a delicious food, and even though it's a rich food, it's a very valuable food. (See raw milk—also wulzen factor.)

Raw cream is the fatty part of the whole milk which rises to the top, after standing, making the milk look top heavy.

If you're lucky enough to own a cow, or if you're lucky enough to have a source for clean raw milk, the raw cream has many uses.

Raw cream, of course, makes delicious butter (see butter section for instructions). It also can be made into scrumptous sour cream (see homemade sour cream), and let's not forget it can make incomparable ice creams (oh dear, see that section too). One also never forgets, if one has eaten it, how raw cream tastes over cereal; whipped or plain with fruit, pudding or other desserts. There are no words to describe it...(Do you sense that I have an aggressive appetite?)

Cream Cholesterol Controversy

Dr. Robert C. Atkins (of carbohydrate fame) says if you eat cream and not eat carbohydrates, it will make you skinny (fat chance - for me) and drop your cholesterol level. Other doctors say if you eat too much cream, period, it can heart-attack you.

The experts are still arguing over the animal fat-cholesterol controversy. Possibly it will be solved by the Millennium—I'll let you know then. (See Lecithin in fighting cholesterol.)

Commercial Cream

The United States Food and Drug Administration has standards for many of the different types of cream if they are shipped in interstate commerce. These standards give minimum milkfat requirements for each type of cream.

General Cream Tip

Cream should be tightly covered at about 40 degrees. The quality is best if stored not more than 3 to 5 days.

Light Cream (Table Cream)

Light cream must have at least 18 percent milkfat according to Federal standards and most state standards.

Tip on Light Cream

For maximum shelf life, do not return unused cream from a pitcher to its original container. Store it separately in the refrigerator, or better, pour only the amount to be used at one time.

Half-and-Half

Half-and-Half is a mixture of milk and cream, homogenized. Under state requirements, it must have between 10 and 12 percent milkfat.

Tips on Half-and-Half

Half-and-Half can be mixed at home using half homogenized whole milk and half table cream.

As with light cream, do not return unused half-and-half to its original container.

Light Whipping Cream

Light whipping cream must have at least 30 percent milkfat under Federal standards of identity.

Tip on Light Whipping Cream

To whip this kind of cream, have both the bowl and the cream well chilled.

Heavy Whipping Cream

Heavy whipping cream must have at least 36 percent milkfat.

Whipped Cream (Raw or Commercial)

1 cup whipping cream = 2 cups whipped cream

1. If you're using raw cream for whipping, it should be at least a day old.

2. To keep the fat firm during whipping, chill the bowl and beaters one or preferably two hours. Prevents an oily texture.

3. For best results using an electric mixer, beat cream at almost top speed until it thickens. Reduce speed; do two jumping jacks, and it should be done. Don't over beat.

4. Don't add your sugar and vanilla until cream has whipped to a medium thick consistency or your cream won't

thicken. That (valueless) powdered sugar works better than that (valueless) granulated sugar as a sweetner. Sweeten to match your sweet disposition. Usually 2 or 3 tablespoons sugar and 1 teaspoon vanilla to 2 cups whipped cream.

5. Don't over whip heavy cream or it will go grainy.

6. Warmer cream than about 50 degrees will quickly turn into butter.

7. If you're using whipped cream for decorating purposes, whip the cream molecules almost to the butter state and force the thick cream through a pastry tube.

8. If you have over-beaten your cream, add 2 or 3 tablespoons cream or heavy milk and continue to beat.

9. You can whip cream in a blender but it's chancey, you could get butter.

10. Whipped cream may be flavored after cream is whipped (never before). Add your preferred flavor in small amounts and whip again slightly. Variations are: ¾ cup fresh fruit; ½ cup honey, jam, coconut or nuts to 2 cups already whipped cream.

Avoid Non-dairy Substitutes for Whipped Creams

Nothing can really take the place of raw whipped cream; however, commercial cream is superior to non-dairy whips. But many popular non-dairy commercial whips are being used. Read the labels. Here is the list of ingredients on the package of the most popular non-dairy whip in a box: sugar, hydrogenated coconut and soybean oils, propylene glycol monostearate (emulsifier—for uniform blending of oils), corn syrup solids, sodium caseinate, whey solids, sodium silico aluminate (prevents caking), hydroxylated soybean lecithin and acetylated monoglycerides (emulsifiers) artificial flavor and color, BHA (a preservative).

Substitutes for Whipped Cream

1. Honey meringue is a delicious topping. Beat 1 egg white until stiff. Continue beating and drizzle in ½ cup honey. Beat until it stands in high peaks.

2. Chill a 13-ounce can of evaporated milk for 11 or 12 hours, and add 1 teaspoon of lemon juice. Whip until stiff. Sweeten to taste.

3. Let light cream (18 to 20 percent) sit in the refrigerator for 2 full days (48 hours) and skim the top off for whipping.

4. Let one package of unflavored gelatin soften for 5 minutes in 3 tablespoons cold water. Dissolve the gelatin in ½ cup hot light (18 to 20 percent) cream.

Add another cup light cream and 1 tablespoon powdered sugar. Chill about an hour and stir in 1 teaspoon vanilla. Chill for 4 or 5 more hours, stirring occasionally. Beat like whipped cream for 5 or 6 minutes.

5. Add 1 cup powdered milk to 1 cup ice water. Whip until thick; then add 1 teaspoon lemon juice, 1 teaspoon vanilla, and sweeten to taste.

Freezing Cream

Cream can be frozen, but has limited use afterwards. Cream to be frozen should also be pasteurized. Thawed cream should be heated first before using in ice cream recipes. The texture of thawed cream makes it unsuitable for use on cereals, etc. It can be whipped, however, and it is used effectively in frozen salads, desserts, etc.

Small mounds of whipped cream can be frozen on a piece of foil (or in ice cube trays). Freeze uncovered, wrap or bag when solid, and return to the freezer. These little dabs of whipped cream can be used in many different ways. They thaw quickly. So put a few on your favorite, almost-ready-to-serve dessert.

Substituting Cream in Baking

If you're baking, and a recipe calls for cream, and you have only milk on hand, you can substitute milk and butter to get proper texture. The famous Rombauer Mother and Daughter cooking team suggests:

To substitute for 1 cup light (20 percent) cream, use ⅞ cup milk and 3 tablespoons butter. To substitute for 1 cup heavy (40 percent) cream, use ¾ cup milk and 1/3 cup butter. This substitution, of course, will not whip.[1]

Commercial Sour Cream

This sour cream is made by adding lactic acid bacteria culture (and other additives) to light cream. It is smooth and thick and contains at least 18 percent milkfat.

Homemade Sour Cream

Put in a glass quart jar:

2 cups cream (20 percent cream or higher)
5 teaspoons cultured buttermilk (commercial type is recommended)

Add buttermilk to 1 cup of cream; shake this mixture vigorously. Then stir in the other cup of cream. Cover the jar and let mixture stand in a warm place (75 to 80 degrees) for 24 hours. (A furnace room works well.) Product may be eaten immediately or is even better if refrigerated for 20 to 24 hours.

Use this sour cream in any recipe calling for commercial sour cream.

(See cream cheeses for low calorie sour cream.)

Non-Dairy Creamer—A Spoonful of Chemicals

Using non-dairy creamers isn't the best choice of so-called foods, as here are the ingredients of one popular brand: corn syrup, vegetable fat, sodium caseinate, dipotassium phosphate, mono-and diglycerides, sodium silicoaluminate, lecithin, artificial flavor and colors....Avoid these artificial products, if possible.

The Butter Battle

I'll tell you about margarine first, because margarine, being lower priced, has almost pushed butter off the shelves. But one must remember that margarine is a completely artificial product. It is full of additives, emulsifiers, and chemicals that in reality, aren't meant for human consumption.

Diacetyl and isopropyl and stearyl citrates[1] camouflaged as "flavor enhancers" are added to margarine. Sodium benzoate, benzoic acid or citric acid[2] may be added as preservatives. (The benzoates are poisons and have actually caused death.) Margarine emulsifiers, such as diglycerides, monoglycerides, etc., don't even have to appear on the label.

One must also be aware that all margarines are hydrogenated and this fact alone makes it a very objectionable product.

They Hide It in the Margarine

Some manufacturer's might try to camouflage the hydrogenation but hydrogenation is the method used to harden the oil.

One company boasts that the corn oil in their product isn't hydrogenated and they are correct; but the one important fact they don't tell you is that the soybean and cottonseed oils in the same product are *hydrogenated.*

The consumer should be aware that any oil that doesn't "run", is usually hydrogenated. The word hardened actually means hydrogenation.

Don't be misled by 100 percent corn oil products. If they are hardened, they are indeed hydrogenated.

You'll Break Your Key

The hydrogenated process given to fats confuses human physiology. Dr. Bicknell explains it this way, "The abnormal fatty acids produced by 'hardening' (hydrogenated) are the real worry. The atoms of the molecule of an essential fatty acid are arranged in space in a particular manner...but hardening may produce a different spatial arrangement, so that a completely abnormal...unsaturated fatty acid is produced. An analogy is ordinary handwriting and mirror handwriting; both are identical but spatially different, so that at best reading the latter is difficult and at worst serious mistakes are made. The same mistakes are made by the body when presented...(with the abnormal) EFA.* Not only does it fail to benefit by them, but it is deluded by their similarity to normal EFA and so attempts to use them. It starts incorporating them in biochemical reactions and then finds they are the wrong shape; but the reaction has gone too far to jettison them and begin again with normal EFA, so they are not only useless, but actually prevent the use of normal EFA. They are in fact *anti*-EFA. They accentuate in man and animals a deficiency of EFA. An analogy is jamming the wrong key in a lock; not only is the lock not turned but the right key is also rendered valueless."[3]

Other researchers report that cancer, arthritus, heart disease, skin disease, arteriosclerosis, (hardening of the arteries) and other degenerated conditions appear to be affected by a lack of EFA.

During hydrogenation, if nickel is used as the catalyst, and any trace of the metal is left in the hydrogenated product, the valuable Vitamin B-6 is possibly destroyed. Deficient Vitamin B-6 is a possible cause of arteriosclerosis.

Hydrogenation also destroys the valuable lecithin, one of mother nature's natural cholesterol fighters.

Whenever you tamper with the natural foods, you tamper with natural body processes.

Can You Afford Butter?

Is margarine worth the lower price you pay? I think not. You cannot afford to use it. It's an artificial product containing ingredients not meant for human consumption, no matter what the manufacturers claim in their advertising. In cooking use ½ cup unrefined oil for every square of margarine.

If butter puts too much strain on your budget, buy unsalted butter (salt it at the table if you prefer the salty taste) made with

---

*EFA—Essential Fatty Acids

sweet cream (read the labels carefully) and make it into
"Economical Butter"—it's inexpensive and low calorie. Also
nuts and seeds make wonderful natural butters. If you still use
margarine, despite the knowledge you now have concerning
the product, it too can be made into more "economical
margarine."

Butter is Better

You mention butter, and most people cringe; because
butter is noted as a contributor to cholesterol. The experts have
differing opinions.

Speculation is when butter is made, the lecithin (mother
nature's fat dissolver) is washed into the buttermilk leaving the
butter without a natural fat dissolver. In the days where
everyone made their own butter, the buttermilk was used in
drinking, cooking, etc., so the "old homesteaders" were
protected by the natural cholesterol—lecithin team, found in
the raw buttermilk. (Commercial buttermilk is not raw buttermilk.)

If you have access to good raw milk, make your own butter,
and drink the buttermilk; then you're protected.

To decrease cholesterol by two-thirds in butter, make
"Economical Butter" (one pound butter = three pounds
economical butter).

Some nutritionists agree that lecithin granules, obtainable
at your health food store (not the lecithin capsules) are effective fat dissipators that you can use on cereals, etc., but they
must be eaten with the cholesterol foods for fat disbursement.

Store-Bought Butter

You even have to be cautious in selecting your commercial
butters. The very best buy in butter is sweet unsalted butter.
Look for these two words on the label, "sweet - unsalted."

"Sweet" tells you the butter is made from fresh, sweet
cream. Other butters not labeled "sweet" are usually made
from stale cream returned to the dairy. The sour cream is
drugged, repasteurized, bleached usually with hydrogen
peroxide and cultured. The cultured cream is "ripened," churned and may be colored with coal tar dyes. Coal tar dyes are
known to cause cancer.

To Salt or Not To Salt

Butter that is unsalted (if you prefer the salt taste, add it) is
a better buy because some butters are over-salted to prevent

the growth of molds and yeasts. Unsalted butter also has fewer additives. Because it spoils more rapidly, it is sometimes found in the frozen food department of grocery stores. It has to be handled a little more carefully at home also. (Freeze it at home and just use a square—¼ pound—at a time.).

Take Care of Your Butter and Oils

Rancid butter, or oils (or anything rancid) can destroy fat-soluble vitamins in the digestive tract, and are considered dangerous to health.

Light, air, and improper refrigeration cause oxidation, and rancidity sets in. So always make certain your butter and oils are wrapped carefully, not exposed to light and have proper refrigeration. Make certain the stores follow the above precautions before you purchase their butter-oil products.

Processed Butter

Processed butter is usually sold in bulk. It is made by rechurning inferior butter with fresh milk to remove foreign flavors and odors.

Make Your Own—It's Better Butter

Use clean whole raw milk to make good butter. Pasteurized milk cannot be used. However, you can pasteurize your cream after it has separated if you're concerned about the product being unsafe. Keep your milk cool and covered for about 24 hours to allow the cream to rise. Skim the cream and cool immediately. You can churn your butter after three hours of chilling. It's advisable to keep the milk from 53 to 55 degrees F. for best results. Higher temperatures will give your butter more of a greasy texture. Lower temperatures will result in a brittle, funny texture.

One quart cream = ¾ pound butter.

If you want to make a large amount of butter, it's best to use a butter churn. If you are making a small amount, and electricity is available, use your blender. If electricity isn't available, shake a bottle (not quite full) of cream in figure-eight motions for faster results.

In using the churn method, the churning should take from ten to 45 minutes depending on the amount you're churning. Your cream will go foamy, then mushy. Proceed more cautiously when mushy because as it grows to the size of large peas it's done. Drain off buttermilk (drink it or use it in cooking) then rinse your butter gently with cool to lukewarm water. If you add salt, add about 1/3 to ½ tablespoon to a ½ pound of butter. Mix in salt with or a wet paddle. Mold into buttersquares and wrap generously in foil or other wrap.

Butter Storage

Homemade butter will freeze up to six months. If no refrigeration is available, butter will keep for six months in *brine*, in a cool place. (Brine = 6 tablespoons salt to a quart of water)

Low Calorie Economical Butter

1 lb. butter = 3 lbs. expanded butter

1 lb. butter*
1 cup cold water
3 cups hot water
2 pkg. unflavored gelatin
1 1/3 cups powdered milk
salt to taste
two or three drops yellow food coloring (optional)

(If you want to make a smaller amount use: 1 cube butter, 1 cup milk, ½ pkg. or 1½ teaspoons unflavored gelatin.)

Directions: Melt butter in a pan placed over hot water (double boiler).
Sprinkle unflavored gelatin in the 1 cup cold water. Add powdered milk to the 3 cups hot water. When butter is melted, add softened gelatin, salt, and hot milk to the hot butter. Heat this mixture over the hot water until the gelatin is dissolved. Add natural food coloring if available. Beat the warm mixture vigorously in a blender for about one minute. (The blender beating prevents the butter from separating from the milk when chilled.) Pour the beaten mixture into containers and chill until very firm. It's ready to eat.
You can expand the butter further, by adding more milk and more gelatin, but you get a butter type custard. Use the above amounts for preferred results. This butter can be frozen.
Add 15¢ to the price of one pound of your butter, then divide by three. This gives the cost per pound of economical

butter. Mine comes to 33¢ per pound. Also this method cuts butter calories and cholesterol by 2/3. One pat of butter or margarine is 95 calories. One pat of this butter is only 33 calories.(Not suitable for frying, but is good as a spread and is good on most vegetables etc. Remember when using in recipes that this butter is 2/3 milk.

Buttery Tips

1. Unsalted butter may be labeled sweet butter or unsalted butter. Some people prefer the unsalted butter flavor.

2. When using whipped butter in place of regular butter in recipes, use 1/3 to ½ more than the recipe calls for if the measurement is by volume (one cup, one-half cup, etc.). If the measurement is by weight (¼ pound, ½ pound, etc.), then use the same amount.

3. Store butter in its original wrapping or container so it won't pick up odor from other foods.

4. Butter can be kept frozen.

5. Butter is sold in one pound, one-half pound and one-fourth pound packages. It is less expensive in larger packages, and the reserve can be frozen.

6. Make butter the first ingredient on a sandwich. It adds moisture and flavor and keeps the filling from soaking into the bread.

7. All butter should be stored no longer than two weeks in the refrigerator, and kept tightly covered to prevent absorption of other food flavors.

8. One pound of butter equals two cups butter.

Ice Cream—The Garbage Dump Food

Ice cream used to be made of wonderful fresh creams, fresh milk and fresh fruits. Today, many leading nutritionists call commercial ice cream "the garbage dump" food—almost anything can go into it. Indeed, many dangerous ingredients are put into commercial ice cream, and can be camouflaged as emulsifiers, food colorings, stabilizers, etc. The government finally passed laws requiring all ingredients of ice cream to be listed on the packages as of the summer of 1973. Check the contents of what you are buying. Your ice cream is possibly loaded with ingredients not meant for man to eat.

Sounds Like a Chemists Lab

Here is just a small sample of what can be added to America's favorite and most consumed, dessert.

Piperonal is used in place of vanilla. This chemical is used to treat lice. (Causes central nervous system depression.)

Diethyl glucol, a cheap chemical, is used as an emulsifier instead of eggs. Diethyl glucol is the same chemical used in antifreeze and in paint removers.

Butyraldehyde is used in nut-flavored ice cream. It is one of the ingredients in rubber cement. (A possible irritant and narcotic.)

Amyl acetate is used for it's banana flavor. It's also used an an oil paint solvent.(Causes headaches, fatigue and irritates mucous membranes.)

Ethyl acetate is used to give ice cream a pineapple flavor. It is also used as a cleaner for leather and textiles. (Its vapors have been known to cause chronic lung, liver and heart damage.)

Aldehyde C17 is used to flavor cherry ice cream. It is an inflammable liquid which is used in aniline dyes, plastic and rubber.[1]

Find the Good Creams

Does that make you sick? So was I. When I first read this information our freezer was bulging with this so-called nutritious dessert.

What can we do? For one thing, we can put pressure on the manufacturers and demand that they give us back our old-fashioned delicious, nutritious ice cream. We can start complaining, write some letters, be heard. However, some ice cream manufacturers make real old-fashioned ice cream. Search them out. There are still a few around. Read their labels.

Back to the Farm

What else can we do? Well, we can start making our own nutritious ice creams at home. Substitue molasses or honey for refined sugars. Make custard ice creams with lots of eggs; use fruit for flavorings. Freezer or tray made-at-home ice creams can be nutritious and delicious with a little know-how and imagination.

Here are some homemade ice cream hints and some delicious recipes:

Hints on Homemade (freezer) Ice Cream

What is more delicious than a perfect batch of homemade ice cream? I can't think of another dessert to top it. And what fun for everybody to get a taste right off the ice cream dasher. Homemade ice cream occasions can certainly be times of family togetherness.

For a perfect batch of ice cream remember that:

Hand churning is usually superior to the electric churn, but some ice cream lovers feel the finer hand-churned texture isn't worth the arthritic arms. (Let each family member take a turn churning including the children—it seems to taste better if everyone takes part in the action.)

There are many recipes for homemade ice cream, and don't hesitate to make up your own. Of course, the more cream you add, the richer and more creamy the end result. Conversely, the less you add, the less creamy and less fattening the ice cream will be. So, you decide.

For a creamier, smoother texture for any ice cream, and to increase yield, make up your mixture the day before. However, many fun batches are a spur-of-the-moment thing so on these occasions the above is impossible. Also never fill your freezer more than ¾ full (ice cream expands as it freezes). And if you're adding fruits or nuts it's advisable to add them in about the middle of the semi-frozen batch, so the yummy additions will not all land at the bottom.

It takes from 3½ to 6 quarts chipped or cubed ice to 1 cup coarse rock salt per batch. It's advisable to pack 1/3 of the freezer with ice first, then start alternating layers with salt and ice.

If your ice cream comes out granular, either you've churned too fast (sometimes a problem with electric freezers), you've filled the freezer too full, or you've used too much salt in freezing.

For best results churn the mixture at 40 revolutions per minute until it pulls, then triple the speed for the next 5 minutes, then drop back to double speed and churn until your arms fall off. (it's worth it.)

Here is the best home freezer ice cream recipe I've ever come across.

Jarold and Peggy Sorenson's Favorite Ice Cream

4 cups milk
2½ tablespoons flour
5 cups cream
2 cups sugar
3 eggs
½ teaspoon salt
2½ tablespoons vanilla

Scald 2 cups of the milk. Set aside. Then mix the flour and sugar, and add slowly to this 1 cup of cold milk. Mix until smooth. Add this slowly to the hot milk and cook, (can use double boiler) stirring over moderate heat for 8 minutes. Beat eggs, adding small amounts of the hot mixture to the eggs. Then add eggs to hot mixture cooking 2 more minutes, stirring (don't burn).

Add cream, vanilla, salt and the other cup of milk to the freezer, then add hot mixture slowly. Freeze.

Our friends served this as Rocky Road Ice Cream adding 3 squares unsweetened chocolate (carob may be substituted), *walnuts, sliced bananas and miniature marshmallows. (Oh me, oh my!) Fresh or frozen fruits added are delicious additions in place of the Rocky Road ingredients.*

(The next two recipes are a good way to use your Eagle canned milks if you have some in storage—use sweetened cream in place of canned milk if desired.)

Don and Margery Horsley's Yummy Ice Cream

1 quart half and half
1 can Borden's Eagle Brand milk
½ gallon milk
2 tablespoons pure lemon extract
1½ tablespoons vanilla
¾ cup sugar

Add all ingredients to home freezer and freeze. Eat, smile and grow bigger.

Fattening But Good Ice Cream

2 quarts half and half (oh, those bulging hips)
2 cans Eagle brand milk
4 eggs
1 cup sugar or honey
1 tablespoon vanilla

Beat eggs, add other ingredients and freeze.

Fruit Lover's Ice Cream (No cream)

6 cups fresh fruit (diced—strawberries are delicious)
1½ cups honey
1 tablespoon vanilla
¼ teaspoon salt
1 cup dry powdered milk
milk (enough to fill freezer ¾ full)

Put all ingredients in blender with just enough milk to work blender. Add mixture to freezer and fill up to ¾ full with milk, stirring. Freeze and eat.

Hints for Freezer Tray Ice Creams

Don't underestimate the yummy *freezer tray* ice creams. The secret of tray ice creams is to beat a couple of times while freezing. And once after freezing. They can be delicious.

Honey Fruit Ice Cream

2 cups milk
¾ cup honey
dash of salt
2 eggs, beaten
1 cup heavy cream, whipped
fresh fruit, 1 teaspoon fruit powder or several fruit cubes

Scald milk, then add honey and salt and cool to luke warm. Gradually add eggs. Cook in double boiler, stirring constantly until mixture thickens, slightly. Cool. Fold in cream and fruit addition and turn into refriferator tray. Freeze until firm. Serves 6.

Blender Fruit Ice Cream

¾ cup heavy cream
3 cups fresh fruit
3 tablespoons honey
¾ cup fruit juice

Whip cream in blender, then transfer to bowl. Blend remaining ingredients smoothly and fold gently into cream. Freeze in ice cube trays and beat twice while freezing. Serves 5 or 6.

Ice Cream (Low Calorie)

½ cup powdered milk
1½ cups water (cold)
3 tablespoons honey
1½ teaspoons vanilla
1 envelope (1 tablespoon) unflavored gelatin
½ cup fruit (optional)

Sprinkle gelatin in ½ cup of cold water. Add rest of ingredients except fruit to double boiler. Heat over water. Add softened gelatin. Stir until dissolved. Add fruit. Pour in freezer tray and let stand 10 minutes before putting in freezer. Freeze until firm. Beat. Refreeze. Serves 5 or 6.

Steamed Wheat Ice Cream
(Yield 3 cups)

6 cups steamed whole wheat
6 cups water

1½ cups dry milk
2/3 cup honey
1 teaspoon vanilla

Mix in blender until smooth. Strain out the bran. Freeze in a tray until firm, then whip to make soft ice cream.

Snow Ice Cream

1 can evaporated milk highly concentrated (reconstituted dry milk works well)

Flavor this with 2 tablespoons molasses or brown or white sugar, dash of salt and any flavoring. Then stir in fresh "dry" pure snow to taste.

Make up your own ice cream recipes. Here are some variations:

Fresh Fruit Ice Creams: Follow any basic ice cream recipe. Omit vanilla. Add any of these fruits (or others) when dessert is partially frozen: crushed or pureed apricots, peaches, plums, strawberries, raspberries, bananas, pineapple, apples with cinnamon, etc.

Fruit Peel Ice Creams: Follow any basic ice cream recipe. Omit vanilla. Then add any fruit peel powder (see fruit peel powder) to taste and freeze like fresh fruit ice cream above.

Nut Ice Creams: Use any chopped nuts, including soybean nuts with any recipe. For mock-nut ice cream, pour milk over about ½ cup soybean grits, add 1 teaspoon pure or natural flavorings. Can use immediately, but it's better to let stand overnight.

Chocolate (carob) Ice Cream: Add carob and Pero powder to taste; stir until smooth. Use as you would chocolate. These are very nutritious substitutes for chocolate.

Caramel Ice Cream: My daughter Heidi discovered that for caramel topping, just spoon molasses over ice cream. It's delicious (not the usual molasses flavor). Also in making caramel ice cream, add molasses to taste, or mix half honey and half molasses.

Yogurt Ice Cream: Use yogurt in place of some of the milk or cream in any ice cream recipe.

Popsicles: Freeze any ice cream or sherbet recipes in popsicle trays or orange juice cans for fun nutritious popsicles.

Milkshakes: Freeze ice cream or fruit cubes. Put cubes in blender and add milk, cream or fruit juice and blend until smooth.

Other Ice Cream Facts and Tips

1. Commercial ice cream along with the "additives" must contain at least 10 percent milkfat.

2. Keep ice cream in tightly closed cartons or tight containers to prevent an "icy" texture.

3. If you store ice cream in your frozen food department, try to use within a week. If you store it in a deep freeze, it will keep for a month or two if temperatures are kept below zero.

4. Ice cream is easier to serve if it's transferred from the frozen food compartment to the refrigerator section a short time before serving—about 10 minutes for a pint and 20 minutes for a half gallon.

5. Some ice creams have egg yolks added. This may be called frozen custard, French ice cream, or New York ice cream. Read labels.

Homemade Ice Milks (Freezer Tray)

Homemade ice milk can be made in freezer trays with any combination the same as ice cream. Ice milk requires a little more sweetner. The secret, don't forget, for freezer tray desserts is to beat twice during freezing, and usually just before serving if soft serve is desired.

Ice Milk (Commercial)

Ice milk is made from milk, stabilizers, sugar, and artificial flavorings. It must contain between 2 and 7 percent milkfat if it is sold in interstate commerce. The soft-serve frozen dessert you can buy at the roadside stand is like ice milk except that it's specially processed to be served soft. Treat ice milk as you do ice cream. See tips for ice cream. The same type food additives present in ice cream are usually present in ice milk.

Sherbet (Commercial)

Sherbet is made from milk, fruit or fruit juice, stabilizers, and sugars. Sherbet has a high level of sugar—about twice as much as ice cream. It must have 1 to 2 percent milkfat. Handle sherbet like ice cream. (Many artificial additives are added to sherbet.)

Water Ice (Commercial)

Water ice is like sherbet except that it contains no milk solids. (Artificial additives present.)

Easy Sherbets and Ices

Try your hand at some fun, homemade sherbets and ices. But to get favorable results remember:

Sherbets may be still-frozen, but if egg whites or gelatin are added, you get a lighter, more frothy result. Also remember that freezing ices dilutes the flavor, so add sufficient flavorings. Never add more than 1 part sweetner to 4 parts liquid, because too sweet a product won't freeze, period. Have you ever tried to freeze honey? No can do.

If you're using a churn or home freezer, follow directions for ice cream method. If you're using freezer trays, always cover your trays with foil, etc. Beat your sherbets while they're quite slushy, and beat a couple of times during freezing. Let thaw 15 or 20 minutes before serving.

Make up your own easy recipes for sherbets, and ices. Here are a few:

Fruit Milk Sherbet

3 tablespoons fruit powder
¾ cup unsweetened fruit juice (to complement fruit)
6 tablespoons honey
3 eggs
½ cup brown sugar
3 cups milk

Beat eggs, add sugar, beating. Stir in all ingredients except milk; then add milk gradually, stirring. Freeze in a tray until slight crystals form. Remove and beat, removing ice crystals. Return and freeze. Yield over 4 cups.

(If using bottled or reconstituted dried fruit, etc., use ¾ cup plus 3 tablespoons of fruit and liquid.)

Your yogurt and buttermilk additions in recipes give you the valuable lactic acid. Here are two examples:

Orange Yogurt Sherbet

1 cup yogurt
½ cup orange concentrate (undiluted)
¼ cup water
1 tablespoon lemon juice
1 tablespoon honey, brown or raw sugar
2 egg whites

Mix thoroughly all ingredients except eggs. Put in freezer tray and freeze until solid. Beat frozen mixture until smooth. Then beat egg whites until stiff, and fold them into the mixture. Return to freezer and freeze. Serves 4.

(You can substitute other juices, fruit cubes, or purees for orange juice.)

Buttermilk Sherbet

¾ cup thawed fruit cubes (fruit puree)
4 tablespoons honey or brown sugar
1 tablespoon lemon juice
1 grated lemon rind or lemon powder (see fruit peels)
1½ cups buttermilk
2 egg whites, beaten stiff but not dry

Blend puree and honey, then add rest of ingredients except egg whites. Freeze in a tray until frozen. Beat frozen mixture until free of lumps and fold in egg whites. Freeze again. Serves 5 or 6.

Children's Delight...

Snow Sherbet

Put fresh dry pure snow (don't compact it) in a bowl, and pour over any fruit juice to taste.

Fruit Ice

1 cup fruit puree (in the summertime put your fresh, raw fruits right in the blender)

Add lemon juice or fruit peel to taste. Add 4 cups water. Freeze until slushy. Beat. Freeze and beat once more. Thaw slightly before serving.

Freeze any sherbets or ices as nutritious popsicles.

Eggs
To Be or Not To Be—Harmful

Fresh farm eggs (if you can find them) are truly a valuable food and should be included generously in everyone's diet, even with their exorbitant rise in price. At a dollar a dozen, eggs are still one of the most economical and excellent sources of protein. Two eggs (at one dollar a dozen) cost approximately 17 cents and give 12 grams of protein, 1180 units of vitamin A, 2.3 mg. of iron, and lecithin, cholin, vitamin B-12, niacin, as well as many other essential nutrients.

The Best Protein in the World

Don't be misled when you compare the grams of egg protein with the amount in other food, since two eggs supply only about 12 to 18 grams of protein (depending on size). This doesn't seem like a lot compared to let's say, the 25 protein grams in a half cup of beans. The difference is in the quality of protein each food has.

The egg is the most perfect protein available for human consumption. Egg protein has nature's most perfect eight essential amino acids and therefore all other protein foods are compared to the egg; it is the standard for judging protein.

For example the egg protein has an NPU (net protein utilization) of 94; whereas the NPU of beans is only 50. Beans have to be sprouted or supplemented with other protein foods to be a good source. Eggs need no supplementing.

The Cholesterol Scare

Eggs have lost their prestige as a healthy food because of the cholesterol scare. But what hasn't been discussed too loudly is that egg yolk is an excellent source of lecithin. Lecithin is a natural cholesterol fighter; it automatically breaks up fat into tiny particles, helping to prevent the fat from adhering to the veins and arteries. That is, if the natural assimilation of lecithin is not interferred with. When oils that are *refined* or *hydrogenated* are consumed with lecithin filled foods, the lecithin is discarded. Use natural, unhardened, unrefined oils as much as possible.

Egging You On

If you eat properly, and avoid much of the commercial man-made foods, eggs can be used generously in your diet. Lecithin, then, can do the job it was originally intended to do—break up fat. Eat the foods provided by Mother Nature, natural wonderful God-given foods. If refined foods were unavailable the experts could retract their original fears about eggs and once again encourage people to put eggs back in their diets.

Much more could be written about the food value of an egg, but let's move on and discuss how to get maximum benefit in raising, buying, cooking and storing this essential food.

I will not attempt to describe the step by step process of raising chickens. But if you can find a little room for a few chickens, by all means, raise your own.

If you'd witness what takes place in plants producing the commercial egg, you'd not only shudder, you might be revolted enough to build a small coop in your own yard.

If you are considering this as an adventure, remember it's advantageous to let chickens roam and peck and scratch in unsprayed fields to their delight. This natural chicken food brings many added benefits to the eggs, such as the valuable Vitamin B-12 and many other natural biobistics. And if there's a rooster roaming with the hens, that's added benefit, usually giving a fertile egg. (Besides a happy henyard.)

It's Only Chicken Feed

About 99 percent of all animal feed contains additives, but many feed outlets will make up mixtures on request without chemicals or drugs. The following formula is a nutritious diet for your own chickens.

If you plan to have a few chickens, contact the agricultural agent in your community for complete instructions and know-how.

For Growing	Pounds	For Laying	Pounds
Corn	240	Corn	300
Wheat	240	Wheat	300
Oats	100	Oats	100
Alfalfa Meal	100	Alfalfa Meal	100
Soybeans	120	Soybeans	100
Gluten Meal	100	Meat Scrap	50
Meat or Fish Meal or			
50% or each	60	Dried-milk powder	20
Cod-liver Oil	8	Bone Meal	20
Limestone	12	Limestone	10
Dried-milk powder	20	Salt	10
Salt	5	Sunflower Seed	50

Let me explain why a few chickens running through your yard would not only be a good investment, but would be advantageous to your family's health.

Bad Eggs? Could Be Two Years Old!

Eggs are highly perishable. Every day eggs lose some of their food value. Did you know that the eggs you buy in the stores could be up to two years old? They now have a technique to enclose each egg in a transparent plastic shell, vacuum-seal it, then use ultraviolet light for sterilization. These eggs have a shelf life of over two years.[2]

Eggs can also be placed in cold storage for months and still be labeled as "fresh."

Commercial eggs are usually washed in a strong solution and dipped in a commercial oil. Washing an egg removes the film Mother Nature put on to protect the porous egg from being infiltrated by bacteria. An egg should be washed only just before using.

Commercial eggs were so pale and watery, the customers complained. So many of the ingeneous manufacturers give the chickens additives to darken the yolks. Even worse, the poor chickens lay eggs with weak shells; so they are usually drugged, given terephthalic acid, then solutions of sodium bicarbonate or can be placed in a hen house where carbon dioxide has been pumped. Drugged poultry or birds inhaling this gas, it was discovered, lay eggs with thick shells instead of weak flimsy shells.[3] Poor chickens!

Buying Eggs

Since most people use store-bought eggs, because of necessity, be aware that so-called fresh eggs are superior to expired eggs, so buy wisely and check expiration dates on commercial cartons. Never buy eggs after their expiration date if possible.

The Best Eggs For Your Money

The color of an egg is unimportant. It doesn't matter if the eggs (especially farm eggs) are white or brown, or if their yolks are light or dark. Just avoid eggs with shiny shells. If you're not certain of the freshness of an egg, float it in a bowl of cold water. If it floats, throw it out. A very fresh egg has a yolk that stands up when cracked into a pan, and a thick rich white. Older eggs will run all over the pan. They are still edible, but have lost considerable food value. A spoiled egg can be determined immediately by a watery appearance and sour smell, when cracked.

A fertile egg will have a tiny dark speck in the center of the yolk. Just stir it in but if you're a fuss-budget, dip it out with the end of a knife or spoon.

Duck, osterich and other foreign eggs, (even small bird's eggs) may be eaten, but they must be absolutely fresh, especially duck eggs. Duck eggs, particularly if not fresh, often carry harmful bacteria. However, the bacteria in these eggs can be destroyed if you cook them for ten minutes or bake them in various cakes, breads, etc. for one hour or more.

Egg Cookery

Eggs should always be cooked on very gentle heat. Never use high heat or over cook any egg dish. Excessive and high heat will invariably ruin such dishes as custards, souffles, etc, because the protein of the egg shrinks and gives you a watery, separated result.

When adding eggs to a hot mixture, add some of the hot liquid to the eggs first, then stir in; this conditions the eggs, so they won't curdle.

Cooking Methods

Anyone can cook an egg. But not everyone can cook one properly. Temperature in egg cooking is of utmost importance.

Poaching

Heat the water to just below the boiling point. Add eggs. Reduce heat and cook gently over low heat for about five minutes, or take off heat completely and let stand about seven or eight minutes, without removing lid.

Fry-Steam

Instead of having grease-soaked eggs; try this preferred "frying" method. This method eliminates tough, leathery whites. Rub your skillet lightly with oil, and place over moderate heat. Add eggs, then put in a couple tablespoons of water, milk or tomato juice. Cover tighly, and cook over low heat until done.

Scrambled Eggs

Add a little milk or cream to eggs, then beat. Oil skillet lightly, then pour eggs into skillet. Add cottage cheese, cheese, chopped vegetables, or some delicious sprouts (see sprouts). You can also cook scrambled eggs in a double boiler, without oiling the pan.

Baked Eggs

Turn oven to 325 degrees. Butter or oil a baking dish or custard cups. Add eggs and one tablespoon of milk per egg. Season to taste, then cover and bake for approximately 18 to 20 minutes.

Omelets

Omelet making is a very rapid process. Make sure you have everything on hand before beginning, and make sure your hungry eaters are seated at the table.

You can make a plain omelet or here's a chance to rid your refrigerator of all your left-overs.

A two-egg omelet serves one person, so increase to desired size.

Two Egg Omelet

2 eggs (at least 3 days old)
2 teaspoons cold water
1 tablespoon butter
Seasoning and filling as desired

Directions for Omelet

Note—You can either add fillers into the egg mixture or use them as a filling for the center. Beat eggs, water, seasoning, etc., until they are mixed well, not fluffy. Preheat pan (cast iron is preferred—cleaned with oil). To get a perfect omelet temperature: heat the skillet to the point where a pat of butter will sputter but not brown as it melts. If it browns, the pan is too hot. Remove brown butter with absorbent cloth or paper, lower heat and try again. When pan has reached perfect heat, roll the butter around to coat inside of pan. Add eggs immediately. Work quickly by stirring eggs and allowing omelet to slide easily without sticking. Smooth omelet with fork, and let it set a few seconds. If adding filling, sprinkle it on now. When sides are done and top is smooth and firm, start folding sides with spatula. Gently fold over once from outer edge to center. If extra puffiness or browning is desired, place under broiler for a few seconds.

Fillers for omelets can include:

Any type of meats, cheese, vegetables or fruits. Foods that are chopped, shredded, or mashed make good fillers and add variety. Use mashed leftover potatoes, or any vegetables. Add leftover chicken, fish, sausage, bacon, etc. To add fresh fruit it's best to slice or mash. Canned fruits should be drained and the juice used in place of the water in the omelet. Dried fruit, soaked about eight hours or overnight, drained and chopped may be added.

Souffles—Careful Now!

Souffles are quite temperamental, but can glamorize leftover food like no other dish; they can be served for breakfast, lunch or dinner. The souffle should always be baked in an oven-proof, straight-sided dish, and kept out of drafts. This dish is delicate and must be cooked and served quickly. Ovens should be preheated; all ingredients should be warmed to room temperature; egg whites should be stiff but not dry; and cream sauces used should be rather firm, heated just to a boil. And for especially light souffles, an extra egg white may be added to every two whole eggs used.

Always butter or grease your baking dish, then dust with flour, powdered milk, etc. Ungreased, undusted sides result in your crusts sticking to the sides and ruining the favored result. Also, souffles require quick bottom heat; if your oven has a top unit, remove it if possible.

If oven heat isn't available, the top of a double boiler makes a suitable souffle.

Fillers for souffles: vegetable and meat souffle fillers should mostly be pre-cooked for best results. They can be chopped, mashed, thickly sliced, grated, etc. (Finely grated raw vegetables will work.)

Basic Souffle Cream Sauce (1 cup)

This sauce is merely a "white sauce" and can be used for creaming vegetables and meats, for gravies and souffles (souffles require the extra thick sauce).

Melt over low heat:
2 (3 for souffle) tablespoons butter.
Add to butter, blending well:
2 (3 for souffle) not heaping tablespoons flour
Stir in very gradually:
1 cup milk

Stir quickly with a wire whisk or big spoon to avoid lumping.

You may add salt and pepper to taste, ½ bay leaf, 2 or 3 whole cloves, some onion or green pepper, etc., for variety.

Vegetable or Meat Souffle

Preheat oven to 350 degrees. (4 servings)

Any precooked, canned (drained) or reconstituted dried vegetables or meats may be used separately or combined: peas, asparagus, corn, mushrooms, oysters, cauliflower, broccoli, etc., (green pepper, carrots, celery, onion, may be used raw if finely chopped or grated). Also left over cooked chopped or cubed chicken, roast beef, bacon, sausage, reconstituted dried meats or soy protein may be added.

Basic Souffle Recipe

(Experiment for your favorite combination)

Grease and dust a 7" baking dish.
Prepare:
1 cup cream sauce (If you're using canned vegetables, use the vegetable juice to reconstitute your milk.)
Bring sauce to boil (don't scorch) and add:
1 cup meat or vegetables (or both)

When mixture is hot, reduce heat and add:
   3 beaten egg yolks
Cook and stir for 1 minute and add:
desired seasonings

   Cool mixture slightly, while beating egg whites. Beat 3 egg whites until stiff, but not dry. Fold gently into the vegetable-meat mixture. Pour into your greased—dusted baking dish and bake for 40 to 45 minutes or until firm. Serve immediately.

Egg Nog

Just put in your blender:
1 cup cold milk or 1 cup cold water and 6 tablespoons (1/3 cup) powdered milk
1 egg
½ tsp. vanilla
1 tablespoon honey or any sugar
scant cup cracked ice
any fruit powders to taste

Blend and serve sprinkled with nutmeg.

Pickled Eggs

Simmer until hard boiled:
   12 eggs
Shell eggs and put 3 or 4 whole cloves in each egg.
Mix till smooth with a little cold vinegar:
   1 teaspoon ground mustard
   1 teaspoon salt
   1 teaspoon pepper

Add the above paste to 4 cups boiling vinegar. Stir generously for about 1 minute. Put eggs in a sturdy glass jar, and pour solution over. Cover the jar and refrigerate for two weeks. Use as desired.

Boiled Eggs Are Not Boiled Eggs

   There is no such thing as a boiled egg—anyway there shouldn't be. Eggs boiled in high rolling heat have green yolks and unappealing texture. Boiled eggs should be re-named, "Simmered Eggs".
   Here is the proper method:

How to Do It

Put unshelled eggs in your pan and cover with cold water. Place the pan on medium heat until it reaches the boiling point. Reduce the heat, then allow to simmer.

Soft cooked eggs should be timed from the time the heat was reduced: room temperature eggs—2½ to 3 minutes: cold refrigerated eggs—4½ to 5 minutes.

Medium simmered eggs should be timed from the time the heat was reduced: room temperature eggs—3½ to 4 minutes; cold refrigerated eggs—5½ to 6 minutes.

Hard simmered eggs should be timed from the time the heat was reduced: room temperature eggs—14 to 15 minutes; cold refrigerated eggs—16 to 17 minutes.

Note—Always put hard simmered eggs immediately in cold water, to prevent discoloring of the yolks.

Shelling Simmered (Boiled) Eggs

To remove the shells from hard-cooked eggs, crack the shells gently, and roll each egg between the palms of your hands. The rolling frees the tough skin away from the egg and makes shelling easier. (Very fresh eggs are more difficult to shell.)

Coddled Eggs

Coddled eggs are similar to simmered eggs. The method varies somewhat: bring water to a full boil, add the uncracked egg gently into the water. Take off the heat. Cover the pan and leave until done. Cooking times:

Soft delicate eggs—5½ to 6 minutes
   Medium (firm) eggs—8 to 8½ minutes
   Hard cooked eggs—30 to 35 minutes

Put hard cooked eggs in cold water to stop further cooking. This prevents yolks from discoloring.

Tricks in Beating Eggs

The Whole Egg

Eggs actually perform at their peak if they are about 72 to 75 degrees(room temperature). This is especially true of eggs you intend to beat. So bring out of the refrigerator those eggs you'll be using and let them sit out a short while.

Unless otherwise instructed, beat your eggs vigorously until they turn a lighter color. Then add them to your batters and recipes—do the same when beating egg yolks.

Egg Whites

Beating egg whites is a very touch and go process. The success of good whites is like the success of a good marriage—it requires certain Do's and Don'ts.

Always have egg whites at room temperature before beating.

Make certain when separating the whites from the yolks that not a speck of yolk gets into your whites. If it does, try to remove the yolk by moistening the tip of a paper towel with cold water and adhering the yolk to the paper. If your efforts are unsuccessful, use the egg for something other than meringue. Meringue is extremely touchy. If one spot of yolk finds its way into the whites, or if your mixing bowl and beaters aren't exceptionally clean (especially from oil residue) the egg whites will stay flat and will not fluff up.

Choose the Right Bowl

Choose a large deep bowl for egg whites (it takes three large whites for one pie). Stainless steel and glass are excellent meringue bowls. A copper bowl will turn your egg whites green when the cream of tartar is added; aluminum will cause the whites to become a dull unappealing gray foam; plastic has a chemical effect that prevents volume.

Start beating egg whites slowly, then increase your speed. You should *never* stop beating once you start. Beat until the whites are stiff (not dry) then sprinkle ¼ teaspoon cream of tartar and a dash of salt on top and beat gently. Then add slowly, in a pencil stream ½ cup honey or 3 level tablespoons of sugar FOR EACH EGG WHITE IN YOUR BOWL.

Professional Meringue Hints

1. Meringue shrinks in cooking, so be sure to take your meringue right to the edge of the pie crust; meringue generously touching the crust prevents shrinking.

2. Never use meringue in which the sugar isn't totally dissolved. Rub some between your fingers to see if it feels grainy.

"Tears" on a pie are caused by grainy (undissolved sugar) meringue. "Tears" are also caused by your eggs not being at room temperature before beating.

3. To avoid burning the "tips" of your pie, brown it on your middle shelf rather than the top.

4. Always cool meringue slowly to avoid cracking and spi.'ting. When meringue is almost done, turn off the oven and open the oven door. The pie will cool gradually in the oven.

5. To prevent meringue from falling (after cooking), dip knife in hot water, and cut the warm meringue (not the pie) into desirable serving pieces.

Egg Yolk Hints

1. Egg yolks are 1/3 fat, so they are natural thickening agents for sauces, puddings, etc. The sauces thicken as they cool.

2. A little cream added to two or three egg yolks will thicken one cup of liquid.

3. Never add egg yolks (or eggs) directly to a hot liquid or they will curdle. Always add a tiny bit of milk or cream to the egg then add tiny amounts of your hot liquid to the yolk. It is then that you can add the yolks gradually to your hot mixture. The mixture will automatically thicken with the addition of the yolks. Never allow the mixture to boil or it will curdle. If this does happen, immediately add some cold milk (preferably cream) and stir; or put pan in cold water and stir. (Best results with sauces are obtained by using a double boiler).

Storing Eggs in the Refrigerator

The storage of eggs is relatively easy if you adhere to a few simple rules. Eggs taken from the nest are covered with a soluble coating that protects the porous egg shell, so it's advisable never to wash an egg; just wipe each off and put in an egg carton and then into the refrigerator. Covered (cartoned) eggs stay fresh longer than uncovered eggs or eggs placed in the refrigerator trays.

To store egg yolks, cover the yolks with cold water, and cover the dish, then refrigerate. The raw yolks will keep up to four or five days. If you prefer longer storage, poach first, then cover and refrigerate. (Chopped or grated poached yolks are delicious as a sandwich spread; as a garnish for vegetables, or in white sauce, etc.)

Store egg whites with a tightly covered lid and use within four days.

Freezing Eggs

Eggs can be frozen but cannot be frozen in the shell. The best method is to separate the yolks from the whites; however, they may be frozen whole. Egg whites freeze well, and can be frozen in quantities or singly. The best method for freezing separate egg whites is to drop each one into an ice cube tray section; freeze them, then put the frozen cubes into a seal-proof bag.

Egg yolks and whole eggs need some doctoring for freezing, or they thaw with a tough unappealing texture.

Break the whole egg or yolk into a measuring cup and add (depending what you'll be using them for) one tablespoon of honey, sugar or corn syrup per cup for desserts; or one teaspoon salt per cup for yolks and ½ teaspoon salt per cup for whole eggs for using in main dishes, etc. It's advisable to label "sugared yolks" or "salted yolks" for cooking purposes. You can thaw eggs in the refrigerator or at room temperature. (Don't use frozen eggs without thawing.) One whole egg equals approximately one tablespoon of yolk and two tablespoons egg white.

Dried Eggs

Dried eggs are very useful, if fresh eggs aren't obtainable. It is not advisable to keep dried eggs in storage any longer than one and one-half years (some companies claim a longer period). It is also advisable to use them only in cooked foods because of possible bacteria danger.

How to Substitute

One whole egg is equivalent to 2½ tablespoons sifted dry eggs and 2½ tablespoons water. Stir egg paste until smooth.

One dozen eggs require six ounces dry eggs and just under two cups of water (1⅞ cups). Beat until smooth. Use your reconstituted eggs immediately—egg paste shouldn't sit longer than five or six minutes.

If you prefer not to make the paste, then just add dry eggs and liquid separately to recipes.

A fresh egg has the ability to hold cakes, cookies, etc. together, but the dried eggs don't seem to have this ability. When using dried eggs in baking, soften ½ to one package of unflavored gelatin in ¼ cup recipe liquid, then heat to dissolve; cool and add to recipe. The baked product will appear doughy, so refrigerate to set the gelatin. This method prevents crumbling.

Dried reconstituted eggs are excellent for scrambling. They have a very appealing cheese flavor. A handful of chopped mung bean (or any) sprouts are a delicious addition to these eggs. Add sprouts as eggs are beginning to thicken. (See *Eating What Comes Naturally* for sprouting ideas.)

Avoid Imitation Eggs

Just recently the highly advertised *Imitation Eggs* hit the market. They resemble dried eggs in texture and taste. Imitation eggs should never replace old mother hen's egg in the diet, as they are not a natural food, and would deprive the user of natural food value. Imitation eggs have cellulose gum, artificial food colors, and potassium sorbate as a preservative. Potassium sorbate has been known to cause irritations of the skin.

More Egg Tips

1. To slice an egg smoothly, dip your knife in water, then slice.

2. To make your bread, rolls, or pastries shine, brush them with one egg yolk beaten with a couple of tablespoons of milk or water.

3. For nutritious additions, poach or coddle an egg in a bowl of soup.

4. Eggs will keep longer, but for maximum nutrition use them within one week.

Part 3

The Grainy
Facts About
Grains

Section I

The Grainy Truths

There is a growing trend, to store wheat and other natural grains and buy wheat grinders. You might not appreciate these words of wisdom until you read the story of flour and its commercial counterparts. But actually You Cannot Make a Better Health and Dollar Investment than to have a mammoth grain supply and your own grinder....Let's go back a few years and see what they've done to our *Staff of Life*.

For centuries wheat, corn, barley, oats, rye, buckwheat, rice and millet have been widely used. Early grain millers crushed the whole grains between two large stones. Fine milling was flour, and course milling was cereal. All of the nutrients were preserved in these grains as no heat was required for this process, and the people thrived.

Delightfully Dead

In the mid 1800's a silk bolting cloth was invented that separated the bran from the flour, depleting the flour. Then, in 1874 a steel roller mill was invented taking the flour through a high heat process, one hundred times faster than the old method. This process further depleted the flour by destroying the grain structure. And because the hot wheat germ gummed up the roller it was decided the *wheat germ* also had to go. When the wheat germ was removed the delighted millers noticed the flour didn't go rancid.

At this point in history (after the steel mill was invented) the incidence of heart disease became a threat. Wheat is a life-giving food. When we remove the life from it, we remove the life from man.

The Minnesota Agricultural Experiment Station recorded that cattle deprived of their vitamin E rations, (wheat germ) appeared to be in perfect health, but suddenly dropped dead of heart disease. When the wheat germ was restored, the deaths from heart disease stopped.[1]

Roller milling also drastically reduces the quality and quantity of wheat protein, especially amino acids, lysine and tryptophan. The fat content is reduced by half. A study at the University of California by Eleanor Baker and D.S. Lepkovsky, brought out further losses of roller milling in vital vitamins and minerals:

Losses in Vitamins

thiamin about 80 percent lost in roller milling
niacin about 75 percent
riboflavin about 60 percent
pantothenic acid nearly 50 percent
pyridoxine about 50 percent

Losses in Minerals

manganese about 98 percent lost in roller milling
iron about 80 percent
magnesium about 75 percent
phosphorus about 70 percent
copper about 65 percent
calcium about 50 percent
potassium about 50 percent

We Must Have Nutritious Food!

A common attitude concerning deprived food! "Well, it has some food value, and that's good enough for me." With this attitude one should ask, "Would you mix ¾ water with ¼ gas and put it into your car?" Certainly not, because it wouldn't run. And neither will our wonderful bodies function on minute "dobs" and "bits" of nutrition. We have billions of cells, in the skin, muscles, liver, lungs, intestines, kidneys, blood vessels, glands, heart and crucially, the nerves and brain, that are begging for food. If sufficient nutrition isn't supplied, these cells, organs and bodily functions degenerate. But what is tragic is that usually we are not aware of degenerated internal problems until it's too late.

After it's Dead—What More Can You Do?

Removing the vital substances from wheat wasn't enough, as the flour was still yellow in color, especially when the new fashionable trend was to have everything white. Sugar had been bleached from brown to white, so why not flour? Flour was also bleached antiseptic white which absolutely delighted the millers. Now they could add moldy, dark and dingy flours and no one could tell the difference. Also flour would store exceedingly well as the bleaching sterilized the flour.

For many years a flour bleach called Agene was used, until England's Dr. Mellanby discovered that Agene caused running fits and mental deterioration in dogs. The Food and Drug Administration *under public pressure* finally outlawed this bleach. But bleaches still in use today are: oxides of nitrogen, chlorine, nitrosyl chloride, chlorine dioxide and benzoyl peroxide mixed with chemical salts.

Nitrosyl chloride is a very corrosive reddish-yellow gas, intensely irritating to eyes, skin and mucosa. Inhalation may cause pulmonary edema and hemorrhage.[2]

Benzoyl peroxide is used as a catalyst for hardening fiberglass resins. It may explode when heated, and has been used to heal surface burns and poison ivy.[3] The chlorine oxide bleaches combined with flour proteins form alloxan. This poison induced diabetes in laboratory animals.

He Wouldn't Feed it to His Pigs

Some years ago Senator W. P. Richardson, of Goshen, New York, made arrangements to get stale white bread from hotels to feed his pigs. Before long his pigs became runty, and diseased. The brood sows had small litters or aborted. Even the chickens began to lay irregularly. The tiny chicks which hatched were so weak that few lived. The Senator began to wonder about the white bread. So he placed two test groups of pigs in separate pens, feeding white bread to one group, and whole wheat and whole corn to the other group. Within three months the pigs which had been fed the white bread were exhibiting the same symptoms as his earlier pigs. Those fed whole wheat and corn remained normal.

The Senator explained: "When I think of my experience in feeding pigs white bread left over from New York City's leading hotels, I am astonished at the indifference which white bread eaters manifest toward so many of their ailments. The counterpart of these ailments on my pig farm, with all their distressing consequences came upon me as a complete surprise. Had my pigs and chickens been eating nothing but white bread, I might have suspected the trouble before so much damage had been done; but they were rooting around and grubbing for themselves, getting lots of other food. I believe the white bread didn't amount to more than half of what they ate, but it was certainly enough to cause a commotion in Goshen. (The commotion: the neighbors not only stopped feeding white bread to their hogs; they also stopped feeding it to their children.)[4]

Is it any wonder consumers of bleached white products could be in health trouble? *The Consumer Bulletin Annual,* 1965, 1966, said today's bread is "...presliced absorbent cotton."

Some Breads Have Over 90 Chemical Additives!!!

Worse yet...bread has been whitened with chalk, ammonium carbonate or alum. And silicones are allowed as glazes. And have you noticed that dark yellow bread? It is usually colored with nitric acid, not egg yolk.

Usually on a bread package they list only one chemical additive: calcium or sodium propionate, used to prevent mold—these two propionates are also used as an antifungal medicine for skin diseases. Or they may just say dough conditioners....Some bread will actually say "no preservatives added"—that is misleading because over 90 chemicals (not necessarily preservatives) may be added to a loaf of bread without being mentioned on the label. No wonder we mope around. We're literally being poisoned.

Remember that these same additives in white bread, white flours and commercial wheat flours may also be present in cakes, cookies, crackers, pastries, doughnuts, biscuits, muffins, waffles, pancakes, noodles, macaroni etc. and any commercial mixes for the above.

Whole Wheat Flour and Bread?

They're Pulling Your Leg!

In writing this book, some of the research was disheartening. But after much consideration it was realized that in the case of food, "ignorance can be damaging." We must respond to knowledge and let it guide us intellectually and healthfully. As this is the case you should be informed concerning commercial wheat products.

Some of the wheat flour on the grocery shelves is just as unhealthy as white flour. Because wheat flour is so perishable, and invites weevils easily, it can receive very heavy doses of fumigation. Commercial whole-wheat flour can be treated in some cases with more than 410 times as much bleach as white flour to resist weevil infestation. Also most wheat bread is mostly white flour. Look at the labels.

However, all commercial whole wheat flours aren't treated this way, check around. I found a very reputable local dealer before I had a wheat grinder, so for my money, this was the best choice.

For top dollar value it is wise to invest in a home electric wheat grinder (look around as some are far too expensive for what you are getting). Also some families in various churches are going in together to purchase grinders. Blenders will also grind small amounts of grains for homemade cereal, but grinding for bread is too hard on your blender. Cracking wheat in your blender sometimes dulls the glass.

Be aware that wheat flour has high nutrient losses, and turns rancid easily if shelved for even a short length of time. So for top nutrition, just grind your flours and cereals as you need them.

What About Enriched Flours, Breads, Cereals, Etc.?

Many people eat "enriched foods" thinking they are getting nutritious foods. In the refining process of grains, 25 known nutrients are almost totally destroyed *(and many more that have not yet been discovered)*. The enrichment program replaces 5 synthetic vitamins and minerals into commercial products. To name a few vitamins (biotin, pantothenic acid, and pyridoxine) and minerals (phosphorus, copper, potassium and manganese) and amino acids (protein) lysine and tryptophan are destroyed and not replaced in commercial flour, bread, cereals, etc. Adele Davis explains "that such flour is 'enriched', just as we'd be enriched by someone stealing 25 dollars and returning 99¢."[5] So, make your own. They are simple, inexpensive and can be made nutritiously. See recipes in this chapter.

About Wheat?

Wheat is an annual grass belonging to the family *Poaceae* and the genus *Triticum*. Within this genus there are 14 species, of which three cover about 90 percent of the world's wheat production. These three are generally referred to as common wheat, club wheat, and durum or macaroni wheat.

Wheat plants vary in size from two to seven feet. Their roots may reach as much as eight feet into the soil, although most remain in the top 12 inches. The plants have long, narrow, green leaves that turn golden as harvesttime nears. The stems, or culms, emerge about two-thirds of the way up the plant. At the top of these stems are the spikes. These contain the kernels, the only part of the plant used for human food.

Each kernel of wheat is only one-eighth to one-quarter of an inch long, and a pound of wheat contains 14,000 to 17,000 of them. The kernel has three major parts: the endosperm, the bran, and the germ.

The endosperm is the source of our white flour. The bran is the kernel's skin and protects the endosperm and the germ. The germ contains the seed of a new plant and would sprout if planted. *Whole wheat flour* includes the bran and the germ, as well as the endosperm.

Facts on Wheat or Grain Storage in the Home

1. Choose Hard Red Winter Wheat.
2. Insist upon grade #2 or better, weighing not less than 60 pounds per bushel, with at least 12 percent protein content.
3. The wheat should be cleaned and free from foreign material and smut, but unwashed.
4. Moisture content should be 10 percent or less. Insects are not able to reproduce in clean grain which has a moisture content of 10 percent or below.
5. Clean, fumigated wheat, hermetically sealed in cans, is available for storage. However, if the wheat you are placing in storage is untreated, these are the two easiest effective precautions to eliminate possible insect infestation.

   A. Spread two ounces of crushed dry ice over the bottom of the can. Immediately put the wheat over the top of the dry ice. After the dry ice has evaporated (about 30 minutes), place the lid on the can. If pressure develops with the can (bulging), cautiously remove the lid for two or three minutes and then replace it. To reduce the condensation of moisture on the bottom of the can, follow this procedure in as dry an atmosphere as possible.

   B. Spread the wheat in a shallow pan at a depth not greater than ¾ inches. Place pan of wheat in a 150 degrees oven for 20 minutes. Keep the oven door slightly open to prevent over-heating. If the wheat is thoroughly heated, all stages of insect pests will be destroyed. This treatment may also be used if the wheat has too high a moisture content.

"Note" Never use carbon tetrachloride; granted it kills the insects, but it also kills the wheat. Freezing wheat for storage adds unwanted moisture to the kernel. Pressurized CO_2 is a good method, but more expensive.

6. Metal containers are best for storage, (mice can chew through plastic) but use those which are not too large for moving. Never place metal container directly on cement or dirt floors—they will rust. Set them on wooden slats or shelves.
7. If wheat is properly stored in a cool, dry place with a moisture content of 10 percent or less, it will keep indefinitely. Wheat which is stored for more than one year, should be turned and aerated at least twice a year (except in hermetically sealed cans). Use old wheat first and replace it with new wheat at harvest time.
8. If wheat has already been thoroughly cleaned, no additional cleaning or washing is necessary before grinding. When cleaning is necessary, follow these steps:
     a. Sieve to remove dust, grit, and other foreign materials.
     b. Wash quickly three or four times in large pan, using ample water.
     c. Spread out and dry thoroughly. (See B above.)
     d. Place the dry wheat in a container and grind as needed. Washed wheat should not be stored, as the moisture content is greatly increased with washing.
9. The quantity of wheat needed will vary according to individual needs. For average consumption of bread and cereal, one year's requirement will vary from 70 pounds for a child to 300 pounds for an adult.

Places around the country where you can get information about wheat:[6]

Colorado Wheat Administrative
  Committee
Mile High Savings Building, Room 300
1636 Welton Street
Denver, Colorado 80202

Kansas Wheat Commission
1021 North Main
Hutchinson, Kansas 67501

Division of Wheat Development,
  Utilization and Marketing
Nebraska State Dept. of Agriculture
Terminal Building
Lincoln, Nebraska 68508

Kansas City Board of Trade
4800 Main Street
Kansas City, Missouri 64112

North Dakota State Wheat
  Commission
316 North 5th Street, Room 521
P. O. Box 956
Bismarck, North Dakota 58501

Western Wheat Associates, USA, Inc.
834 American Bank Building
Portland, Oregon 97205

Wheat Flour Institute
14 East Jackson Boulevard
Chicago, Illinois 60604

American Institute of Baking
400 East Ontario Street
Chicago, Illinois 60611

Minneapolis Grain Exchange
400 South 4th Street
Minneapolis, Minnesota 55415

U. S. Department of Agriculture
Office of Information
Washington, D. C. 20250

Oklahoma Wheat Commission
423 South Pierre Street
P. O. Box 549
Pierre, South Dakota 57501

National Association of Wheat
  Growers
1030 15th Street, N.W., Suite 1006
Washington, D. C. 20005

American Bakers Association
1120 Connecticut Avenue, N. W.
Washinton, D. C. 20036

Millers' National Federation
1114 National Press Building
Washington, D. C. 20004

Chicago Board of Trade
141 West Jackson Boulevard
Chicago, Illinois 60604

Eat the Whole Grain

Whole grains give us valuable sources of nealy all the B vitamins, vitamin E, quality protein and those needed unsaturated fatty acids.

Whole grains are indeed a vital food, and the less that's done to a natural grain the more the nutrients are retained. Whole grains are more nutritious than cracked or ground varieties, but of course we need variety in our diet. You can also buy other grains to mix with wheat.

Everything You've Ever Wanted to Know About Flour

Flour is the most important ingredient in home baking. It is the framework of almost every food you bake. Wheat flour is unique.

Flour made from wheat should be used in all your baking but especially for bread making because it contains a special substance called gluten. Gluten is made up of insoluable proteins found in flour, chiefly gliadin and glutinen. The first step in making of bread is the hydration of gluten in the dough mass by mixing water with flour. When we stir and knead flour with liquid, the bands, fibres and sheets of the elastic gluten form the supporting tissue of the loaf, much like a framework of chewing gum. These stretch to hold the bubbles of gas produced by the yeast. The heat of the oven sets the gluten so that the loaf retains its shape. Without gluten you cannot make satisfactory yeast breads.

So let it be known that there is no other grain that makes better bread than good old Mr. Wheat. Wheat flour is the king of universal bread making. The wheat personality has the wonderful gluteness elastic quality that no other grain can claim.* Rye, barley, rice, corn, millet, etc., are no match in the texture or gluteness powers, for King Wheat. He will let them be a part of his troop but he makes it well known that he is top Kernel.

Stone Ground Wheat Flour Hints

1. Stone ground (very fine) wheat flour can make delicious, light breads, rolls, cakes, cookies, pastries, pie crusts and even sponge cakes to duplicate any white flour products.

2. Whole wheat bread has not been made by many homemakers, because of possible poor flavor, texture and quality. They imagine it to be heavy, grainy texture and not palatable. I've proven in my "Food Survival" classes that homemade wheat bread can be delicious. Many women couldn't believe the texture and taste of wheat bread. Many thought it was made of half white, half wheat flour.

3. Use stone ground whole wheat flour in all your baking. You can *substitute whole wheat flour for white flour.* Just use ⅞ cups whole wheat flour for every cup white flour.

4. Whole wheat flour should not be ground for storage. Store your wheat and grind your flour as you need it. Many vital nutrients are lost in wheat flour that is stored. Air will oxidize your vitamins, and the oil in the wheat germ goes rancid very easily. Losses of vitamin E in stored wheat flour are high.

5. All flour can be frozen.

6. Wheat germ should always be refrigerated.

---

*"Note" There are other grains more nutritious than wheat but they lack the gluteness power, and the hard kernal for infinite storage life.

How to Test Flour for Gluten

To determine a high gluten flour take two different flours (one cake flour, the other wheat flour, etc.) and add exactly the same amount of water, enough to make a smooth wheat dough. The high gluten wheat flour really absorbs water. So after absorption, notice that the wheat flour will be firm, whereas the cake flour will be very soft and sticky. Also the reverse, if you add enough water to make the cake dough just right, the wheat dough will be too stiff and not smooth and elastic.

Other Flours

Brown-Rice Flour

Brown-rice flour can be added to other flour. Add 1/5 cup brown-rice flour to 4/5 cup regular flour.

Graham Flour

Graham flour (a wheat flour) sometimes called whole-kernel flour because it's so coarsely ground can be used preferably to make bread. If the recipe calls for 1 cup whole wheat flour, use ⅞ cup graham flour, or more if desired.

Oats or Oat Flour

Steel-cut oats are nutritionally superior to rolled oats, but more expensive. In making oatmeal bread you may use 1/3 cup oatmeal to 2/3 cup flour. Soften oats first before putting in bread dough by covering them with boiling water. When mixture is cool, add it to other ingredients.

In making cookies 3 cups oats may be used for every cup of flour.

Peanut Flour

Peanut flour (like soy flour) in some aspects is 10 times more nutritious than wheat flour. Add 2 tablespoons to ⅞ cup of wheat flour, for breadmaking or other baking.

Semolina (flour)

This flour is a cream-colored granular, high protein flour used to make commercial wheat pasta. If you have problems making homemade pasta (pasta not keeping its shape) your flour usually has a low gluten content.

Soy Flour

Soy flour contains almost 10 times more protein than wheat flour. You can substitute 1/5 of the whole wheat flour for soy flour, or 2 tablespoons to each ⅞ cup wheat flour. Be aware that soy flour causes heavy, fast browning of baked products so watch your oven when soy flour has been added.

Other Nutritious Flours

All of these flours below can also be added to your baking, etc. *Add 2 tablespoons of any of them to make 1 full cup of wheat flour,* unless otherwise stated:

> *Barley flour*
> *Bone meal (add just 1 tablespoon to a cup of flour)*
> *Brewer's yeast (add 1 teaspoon to make 1 cup flour)*
> *Buckwheat*
> *Cornmeal*
> *Cottonseed flour*
> *Flaxseed meal*
> *Gluten flour*
> *Lima bean flour*
> *Millet flour*
> *Millet meal*
> *Potato flour*
> *Rice bran*
> *Rye meal*
> *Soy meal*
> *Sunflower seed meal*
> *Wheat bran*
> *Wheat germ*

Commercial Flours

White flour is deprived flour, milled by finely grinding the endosperm of wheat after the bran and germ have been removed.

All-Purpose Flour

Commercial all-purpose flours are deprived refined flours prepared for home use to make a complete range of products—yeast breads, quick breads, cakes, cookies and pastries. Such flours may be made from low-protein hard wheat, from soft or intermediate wheats, or from blends of hard and soft wheat.

Cake Flour

Commercial cake flours are milled and *refined* from low-protein soft wheat for baking cakes and pastries. This flour has many unhealthy additives.

Gluten Flour

Gluten flour is wheat flour especially milled to have a high gluten and a low starch content. It is used mostly by bakers for making dietitic breads, or mixing with other flours of a lower protein content.

Self-Rising Flour

Commercial self-rising flour is all-purpose *refined* flour to which leavening and salt have been added. One cup of self-rising flour contains the equivalent of 1½ teaspoons baking powder and ½ teaspoon salt. If your recipe hasn't been adjusted for self-rising flour, omit the baking powder and salt. Self-rising flour is not recommended for popovers or egg-leavened cakes; however, because excess leavening will cause the product to over-rise and collapse.

Unbleached Flour

Unbleached flour is all-purpose flour which is aged and bleached naturally by the oxygen in the air. Aged flour is more golden in color and more nutritious than chemically bleached flour. Unbleached flour is usually a higher-protein flour; therefore, it is ideal for breads. If you use white flour, always use unbleached.

Storing Flour

Flour should be stored in a clean, airtight container in a cool place. If flour is allowed to lose some of its natural moisture to the air, it acts like a sponge, absorbing more than the normal amount of liquid from the batter or dough. If the batter or dough made with dry flour becomes stiff, add more of the liquid called for in the recipe—a little at a time—until the desired consistency returns. When making yeast breads, judge by the *feel* of the dough rather than by the amount of flour used.

Humid weather may cause unusually soft, sticky doughs. To adjust for this, add more flour—a little at a time—until the dough returns to normal.

Freezing Flour

Flour may be frozen for long term storage. This is especially helpful for dark flours which contain the oil-rich germ that can become rancid if not stored properly. Wrap the flour carefully in moisture-vapor-proof material before freezing.

Section II

The Magic of Yeast

Yeast is a basic ingredient of most breads known throughout the world. It provides the magic which causes the dough to rise to make a tasty, easy-to-chew product. Without it, the bread would be hard, flat and unpalatable. Yeast is a living plant so small that if 4,000 yeast plants, or cells, were placed side by side, they would measure about an inch. However, even though we cannot see these tiny cells, except with a microscope, they are living all around us...in the air, in the ground and on the fruits and leaves of many plants. Not all of the yeast abundant in the nature is suited for bread making and today our yeast is cultivated and scientifically grown in manufacturing plants.

In the manufacturing plant, a single strain of yeast is carefully selected for production, using a powerful microscope to select the healthiest and most vigorous one. From this single cell through careful planting and feeding comes the quality yeast for the consumer market, whether it is sold as compressed yeast in cakes or as active dry yeast. Active dry yeast is a fairly recent development which came about when it was discovered that the life of yeast could be extended by drying it under proper conditions without affecting its ability to make bread rise. The secret of the process is that the yeast cells go into a resting stage and remain that way for months until warm liquid is added to the yeast. Then it is again active and able to make dough rise through the production of carbon dioxide gas.

In the making of bread, yeast works with the sugar in the recipe to produce carbon dioxide, the latter being the familiar gas that makes soda water "fizz." This action of the yeast on sugar is a form of fermentation and continues throughout the "raising" periods until the yeast plants are killed by the heat of baking. As the bubbles of carbon dioxide expand throughout the dough and cause it to rise, the loaf assumes its characteristic porous appearance. In the process of baking, the dough becomes set and the carbon dioxide is driven off as a gas.

In addition to the raising power of the yeast, the yeast plants also work on the gluten of the flour, conditioning it, making it soft and elastic and rendering it more easily digestible. This is why the dough is allowed to rise before it is put into the pans. The yeast also helps give the bread its characteristic pleasing flavor and fragrance in baking.

The Discovery of Yeast

Discovery of the first leavened (raised) bread was an accident and is believed to have occurred in Egypt around 5,000 years ago, As one story goes, a baker in a royal household set aside some dough made from flour, sugar, and water and forgot about it. By the time he remembered the dough, it had soured. He tried to cover up his mistake by mixing the sour dough with a fresh batch. When this new dough was baked, it developed into a lighter bread than had ever been produced.

What the Egyptian baker didn't know was that some wild yeast from the air had crept into his dough and started to ferment the sugar, making air bubbles that caused the dough to rise and puff up. Although a new breadmaking process had been discovered, the action of the yeast wasn't explained scientifically until the 17th century.

Anyway, yeast was discovered, and now we have light wonderful breads; an important addition to our international tables.

Yeast is Fun to Use, But Remember:

1. Heat kills yeast. Your yeast should be dissolved in water that's warm, never hot.
2. Cold retards yeast action. So if you want your bread to rise slowly, use cool liquid, and keep in a cool place—even a refrigerator.
3. The mineral content in hard water, speeds up the rising process of bread.
4. Lower altitudes require a longer bread rising period. Breads made in high altitudes, require less yeast and shorter rising periods.

5. Soft wheat rises faster than hard wheat. Hard wheat makes superior bread. Soft wheat makes superior pastries.

6. Yeast performs best in temperatures from 75 to 85 degrees. Undesirable organisms can grow in temperatures higher than 85 degrees.

7. Yeast starts to slowly activate at 50 degrees, but really thrives at 75 to 85 degrees. It starts to die at about 120 degrees, and is powerless at about 142 degrees.

8. Brewer's yeast is not a leavener. It is a nutritional food supplement, so don't try to make it perform the regular yeast function. Brewer's yeast will *NOT* make bread rise.

9. Dry yeast will keep for several months (some claim up to two years) in a glass jar in the refrigerator.

10. One fourth ounce yeast raises 2 cups of flour in 1½ to 2 hours. One-half ounce will raise 14 cups of flour in about 6 or 7 hours.

11. Never use salt water to soften yeast. It inhibits it; add salt later.

12. A little bit of sugar expedites yeast acitivity, but too much hinders the yeast growth.

13. If dough is allowed to rise and fall too many times, the yeast energy uses itself up, and then there's not sufficient rising power when it's most needed—during baking.

14. Potato water hastens yeast activity, adds nutritive value, adds keeping qualities, but gives a moist, coarse bread texture. It's worth adding, however.

15. It isn't advisable to use whole milk for breadmaking as the fat of the milk coats the yeast, and prevents it from softening. Butter also inhibits yeast.

No Yeast? Try the Following

1. Bread will rise without yeast if allowed to sit in a warm place (not over 85 degrees) from 20 to 24 hours.

2. Prepare a watery mash of cooked potatoes and water and expose it to the air for several days. Wild yeast will develop on this mash. (To help the process along, if available, rinse the haze of wild yeast that forms on a bunch of grapes and mix into the mash.) Use enough of this yeast in a recipe to make your dough rise.

3. A chip from an oak tree makes bread rise. Be sure to remove the chip before baking or you could get a mouth full of slivers.

4. Make "No Start" Sour Dough Bread. (see below)

5. If you have a tiny bit of yeast you can use it indefinitely by making a sour dough starter (See Sour Dough).

6. Make Wild Yeast (below—be aware that wild yeast is from the air and is uncontrolled, giving it unstable rising power and sometimes an off flavor.)

Sour Dough ("No Start")

See "starter" suggestions in "wild yeast."

Sift together:
  5 cups flour
  2½ teaspoons salt
  2½ tablespoons honey or sugar
Add and stir will:
  4 or 5 cups potato water

Use a large crock as mixture will bubble up. Let sit in a warm temperature (85 to 100 degrees) for about 2 days. (If you have a little yeast, it can be added—won't take as long to rise.)

Wild Yeast

3 cups flour
3 cups warm water
1 tablespoon honey

Mix all ingredients and place in glass container, bottle or crock. Leave uncovered. Let mixture stand in warm place for five days. Stir 3 or 4 times a day, allowing the air to activate the mixture. Small bubbles will form and it will smell yeasty.

Wild yeast is used in varying proportions in each recipe, so experiment for best results. One cup wild yeast is equivilent to about 1 tablespoon yeast. Also this yeast takes several hours for bread to rise....The fifth day (2nd day for sour dough) after you have used some yeast as a "starter", replace the starter by using equal parts of flour and water. In another 24 hours the yeast will bubble and be ready to use again. Store the yeast in the refrigerator with a tight lid. Shake it often. To start the action again, add 3 tablespoons of flour and 3 tablespoons water and stir. Some say the yeast spores crusted around the edge are good for you. Other say, not so. You decide.

Commercial Yeast

There are two types of commercial yeast: Instant Blend Active Dry Yeast and Compressed Yeast.

Dry Yeast

Instant Blend Active Dry Yeast usually comes in foil packages or bulk jars or cans. These are usually dated, so check dates.

Directions

1. Unopened dry yeast needs no immediate refrigeration (See Yeast Storage).
2. To dissolve sprinkle on top of warm (never hot) water (110 to 115 degrees).
3. If blending with your mixer you may use flour and up to 120 degrees liquid.

Compressed Yeast

It usually comes in 2/3 ounce or ⅝ ounce foil-wrapped cakes. Yeast is good when a light greyish tan color but darkens as it loses quality. When it's brown it's old. A freshness test is to add equal amounts of yeast and sugar. Fresh yeast immediately turns into liquid.

Directions

1. Must be refrigerated—keeps about two weeks.
2. Dissolve in LUKEWARM liquid (80 to 90 degrees) for about 5 or more minutes.

How to Interchange Instant and Compressed Yeasts

1. One package Active Dry Yeast equals one ⅝ ounce cake compressed yeast. Two teaspoons dry yeast equals the 2/3 ounce cake.

2. One 4 ounce jar of Active Dry Yeast equals 16 packages Active Dry Yeast or 16 cakes Compressed Yeast.

3. One 1-pound 12 ounce can (tomato juice size) is equal to 64 packages active dry yeast or 64 cakes Compressed Yeast.

"No Dissolve" Yeast

There's a new yeast on the market you don't have to dissolve before adding to your recipes. The Colorado Wheat Administration gives the following tips on this new product:
How to Adjust your own Yeast Recipes to the

"No-Dissolve Method"

The new no-dissolve Yeast saves time and the use of thermometers. You will find the dough itself is also lighter.

You can make all your yeast recipes by this method with no ingredient change. Simply follow these directions:

1. Measure all ingredients for your recipe.
2. Thoroughly mix undissolved yeast with 1/3 of the flour and all other dry ingredients.
3. Heat liquids and shortening over low heat until warm.
4. Add liquids to dry ingredients. Beat 2 minutes at medium speed of electric mixer, scraping bowl occasionally.
5. Add about ½ cup flour, or enough to make a thick batter. If eggs are used, add now. Beat at high speed about 2 minutes, scraping bowl occasionally.
6. Stir in additional flour as needed and proceed according to recipe instructions.

Yeast Storage

Sealed or unsealed dry yeast doesn't have to be refrigerated immediately, but will store much longer if refrigerated or frozen. You may store sealed yeast on the shelf, but it's advisable not to store it without refrigeration any longer than one year. Compressed cake yeast must be refrigerated and will keep up to two weeks. It will freeze up to two months.

To Test Yeast Action

Put 1 teaspoon of yeast in ½ cup of warm (not hot) water. If the yeast is good it will start to thicken, usually coming to the top and forming a velvety look. Give it plenty of time to grow before you decide it's not good.

Making Homemade Bread

It's Fun, Economical and Very Nutritious.

There can't be any domestic endeavor more satisfying than baking your own bread. It's easy, economical and fills the rooms with a mouth watering aroma, giving the house a feeling of unmatched hominess. I guess one of the nicest compliments I've received was from one of my daughter's friends. She said she loved to come to our house because it always smells soooooo good. She happened to say that the day I was baking bread.

My sweet mother exposed me to breadmaking. I remember as young children how we looked forward to the days mother made bread. We would all rush home from school and sit around our mammoth table and eat gigantic pieces of hot homemade bread with butter dripping through our fingers. That same night we always had fried scones for supper. How we loved those days.

Commercial Bread—50% Air

Breadmaking can save you more money at the super market possibly than any other expenditure because of the quantity eaten. An average loaf of commercial bread weighs from one to one and one-half pounds. An average loaf of homemade bread weighs three to four pounds. So see what you are paying for in commercial bread—50 percent air.

Commercial bread costs (at this printing) up to 80¢ a loaf, and still going up, up, up in price. You can bake your own for 10¢ to 12¢ a loaf, with no preservatives and much more food value especially if you have your own wheat grinder. If you buy your flour (whole wheat) at the store, you can still make bread for 15¢ to 20¢ a loaf, which is a considerable savings. We discovered that an electric wheat grinder actually pays for itself in a few months' time, by grinding your own flour.

Baking Bread Is As Easy As Baking a Cake

Also if you can make a cake you can make bread—batter bread. It has a more open texture, but it's far superior to store bread, in terms of food value. My family actually prefers kneaded bread, but when circumstances won't permit, I merely make batter bread.

If you absolutely don't have the time or patience for this domestic endeavor, then it is worth the expense to buy an automatic bread maker. A bread maker also pays for itself in a very short time—not only in dollar value, but certainly in health value.

The Basic Ingredients in Bread

These basic ingredients are necessary for good bread: flour—water—yeast—a sugar—salt—oil

Flour—made out of wheat is the basis for bread, (See "Why Wheat Flour for Breadmaking.") but we add other ingredients for definite reasons.

Water—needed to create the dough.

Yeast—makes the bread light and airy (see about yeasts).

Honey, Molasses or Sugar—(add just a little to the yeast) furnishes the food for the yeast. This forms the gas which makes the dough or batter rise. It adds flavor and helps the crust to brown as the bread bakes.

Salt—(optional) brings out the flavor of the bread. It controls the action of the yeast, slowing the rate of gas formation. Don't add salt directly to the liquid dissolving the yeast as it will retard the yeast action too much. Add it later.

Oil—The oil helps make bread tender, helps keep the baked item soft and gives the bread a soft, silky crumb.

Fancy It Up!

What else can you add to bread?

Add anything, almost! The day you clean out your

refrigerator is the day you should make bread. All fresh leftovers can go into bread plus many other ingredients:

—Gravy, chili, stew, and meats, vegetables, fruits, vegetables or fruit peelings (see fruit peelings), vegetable or fruit juice, cooked cereal, cheese, eggs, nuts, seeds, sprouts, any other grains, soy beans, soy flour, molasses and the list could go on and on....Just put any nutritious foods in your blender and add them to your bread. In my "Food Survival" classes, I give the ladies a sample of homemade bread and inform them they are eating a slice of the most nutritious bread in the world. And it's a fact, when you eat my bread, it's like eating a meal. Every bite offers foods from the "Basic Four."

What About Bread Pans?

Glass, dull (anodized) aluminum, or dark metal loaf pans are ideal for baking bread. These type pans absorb the heat. A shiny bread pan should be dulled. Do this by baking for 5 hours at 350 degrees (to conserve energy, dull your pans while baking something else too).

Breadmaking Hints

1. It isn't necessary to sift flour for making bread, unless recipe so specifies.

2. You can use almost any liquid in breadmaking. Sprout liquid, skim milk whey, skim milk, potato or vegetable liquids, etc. are excellent in bread, rolls, cookies, etc.

3. Plain water added to bread makes crusty breads with a good wheaty flavor, but any of the above, add extra nutrition.

4. Skim milk added in breadmaking makes a bread with a softer crust and a velvety, creamy, wheat crumb that browns easily when toasted.

5. Never put all the flour in a recipe at once. You don't necessarily have to use all of your flour either. When dough is soft, and easy to handle—that's enough flour added.

6. A relatively new theory in breadmaking is that the wheat bran will soften if given a chance to absorb moisture. By softening the bran, the dough has more nutrition, more volume, more elasticity, much better texture, and will result in less dry and crumbly bread. So make your bread doughs (omitting yeast), let them sit several hours (overnight is ideal), then add your yeast, knead, and proceed as usual.

7. For uncrumbly bread add a tiny bit of unflavored gelatin to the cold liquid to soften. One third package (1 teaspoon) for

about every five loaves. It dissolves during baking. Don't add more than this or your bread will be doughy; if this happens, refrigerate it to set the gelatin. Add even less gelatin to batter breads.

8. If you want quick yeast breads—just add more yeast. Yeast adds the nutritive value of the bread and makes it rise more quickly.

9. A yeast taste in bread isn't from adding too much yeast; it's from bread being too warm during rising.

10. You can get away with letting your bread rise just once even if bran hasn't been softened previously, but a much better bread results if you let it rise twice to allow the bran to soften.

11. Also don't make your bread doughs too stiff. Make them just soft enough to handle. At this point if the bread still seems too sticky, incorporate oil into your bread rather than additional flour for uncrumbly results. Soft dough makes a better bread.

12. Soft dough makes superior bread but soft dough is difficult to handle. Make a large canvas pillow case to slip on your bread board or just put a large piece of canvas on your table for kneading bread (allow 5 or 6 inches for washing shrinkage). This eliminates oiling your table, and bread sticking. Fold and keep canvas in a plastic bag in the refrigerator. You may use several times before washing.

13. If your bread is streaked or striped, it needs more kneading, unless you like zebra bread.

14. If your dough doesn't rise your yeast is too old, or your water was too hot and it killed your yeast, or your dough is so stiff the elastic walls can't stretch for lack of moisture.

15. If you bang your dough against the cabinet and table it cuts down kneading time.

16. Put bread next to a furnace for rising or turn on your oven for one minute for about an 85 degrees temperature. If your stove is gas, the pilot light usually makes the oven just right. Set also by a sunny window or by a warm fire.

17. Don't fill bread pans more than ½ full.

18. Prolonged rising of bread can cause fermentation. This gives your bread a yeast flavor, and coarse open texture.

19. Rich doughs are baked at 350 to 375 degrees to prevent over-browning.

20. Breads increase quickly in volume during the first 15 minutes of baking generally known as oven spring. Never open the oven door during this time as the blast of cold air (pop!) can cause bread to collapse.

21. Bread which has too many holes has been cooked at too low a temperature, or has over-risen.

22. If your bread looks lopsided, uneven, or unattractive you've possibly used old misshapen pans, too small a pan or cooked bread at too high a temperature.

23. Keep hot bread away from drafts which cause shrinkage.

24. When cutting homemade bread never cut when hot, unless using an electric knife, or it will have a doughy texture. Tear the hot bread apart for best results. When cutting cool bread, use an electric knife if available, especially if you bake in bulk. Slice the bread before freezing because you can use it (toasted) right out of the freezer without thawing.

25. In sturdy breads such as French or Italian you only use three ingredients: flour, water and yeast.

Step by Step Breadmaking Procedure

1. Have breadmaking ingredients at room temperature.

Mixing

2. Mix your bread ingredients together (at night if possible) except yeast and let set overnight.

3. The next morning, soften your yeast in a small amount of warm water, add the softened yeast to your mixture and proceed normally.

Kneading

4. Start to knead your bread, when the thoroughly mixed dough no longer sticks to the sides of the bowl. Or...

My method: at this point I put two cups of thick bread batter into nests of flour. (I use a small clean plastic bucket, half full of flour, and burrow my fist into the flour to make the nest.) Pour the two cups of batter in the nest and saturate and mix the batter with flour until it can be handled. Then stack the piles of soft dough on a clean, oiled table or piece of clean, floured canvas.

5. To knead, fold the dough in half toward you. With the palms of your hands push dough away, toward you, away. Turn dough every which way and push, press and punch the dough (the punchier you get it the better).

6. Knead the dough thoroughly to work gluten (the elasticity). Incorporate more flour only if absolutely necessary, but remember a very stiff dough results in crumbly bread. A

softer dough is preferred. So if dough is still difficult to handle (firm but sticky) add oil rather than flour to the dough.

Kneading breaks the large gas pockets into small uniform ones. The more uniform the tiny pockets, the better the texture. So knead it, bang it against the cabinet, and beat it with your fists. (I guess that's why I've never needed a psychiatrist. I take my frustrations out on my bread—really, it's excellent free therapy.)

I will never forget the darling petite foods teacher who taught at Utah State University, Miss Rowland. She gave us a breadmaking demonstration I've never forgotten. Her tiny five foot frame and petite hands took hold of a massive pile of bread dough, and on tip toes, beat the dough on the cabinets, tossed it around the room, and slammed it forcefully with her fists. "This, girls," she exclaimed, "is how to get prize bread." And it was. Every loaf was perfect and we yummed every bite.

7. After kneading is finished, oil the surface of the dough. This prevents dough from cracking or dying out.

8. Cover dough with a damp warm cloth or a lid, etc. Put the dough in a warm 80 to 85 degrees temperature. Temperatures above 85 degrees tend to encourage foreign bacteria.

Remove cover from dough. Do the finger tip test. Since the dent you made with your finger tip in the dough remains, you know it has doubled and is light enough to shape.

Punch the dough down. Then turn it out of the bowl onto your pastry cloth. When dough rises, bubbles form in it. Punching the dough down breaks up the large bubbles into many small ones. Kneading bread gives it or rolls a fine texture.

9. Don't let your dough rise too high, before you punch it down or this can damage gluten. (Poke a finger in the dough—if the hole doesn't close in, it's ready. If it closes in, it needs to rise longer.) Also, bread that rises too high after it's put into the pans can go flat and have an open course crumbly texture. NEVER let it rise to double in bulk for the last rising, because it also rises in the oven. Not quite double in bulk is best. Also, don't incorporate any flour into the dough once fermentation has begun.

To Shape Loaves

10. In shaping loaves if dough is a little sticky, rub hands and table with oil—never use more flour at this point. Roll an oblong piece of dough out flat, to force out the gas bubbles. Fold both outer sides to the center, separately, and press with the palm of your hand and seal. Seal all edges to prevent gas from escaping during rising. Roll firmly like a jelly roll and put the overlap in the bottom of well oiled pans. Let rise in the pans until not quite double in bulk. No more. No less, if possible. If it rises too much, it is better to reshape loaves and let it rise the third time.

Baking

11. Through trial and error, it has to be said that no two bread doughs nor no two ovens bake alike. You have to experiment for good results. Due to my husbands employment, we move about every 18 months, and every new home has a different oven. Invariably, I have to gear my breadmaking to my new oven. In one oven I baked my bread to 375 degrees for 50 minutes. My present oven requires 350 degrees for 45 minutes. (Instead of analyzing yourself, put your oven in analysis.) Get to know how it bakes—so, experiment.

BATTER BREADS—Use a high temperature (about 425 degrees) at the beginning of batter bread baking. This crusts the bread before it has a chance to fall. Reduce the heat after about 15 minutes.

BREAD IS DONE IF:
—the aroma overpowers you, the crust is golden brown, the loaf has shrunken from the sides of the pan, it sounds hollow when tapped, or if it falls out of the pan into your mouth.

Bread Has Personality Too

Bread can take on *different* personalities.
—For shiny bread, brush top of dough with beaten egg or

egg white mixed with a bit of water.

—Soft crusts result if dough is brushed with milk or butter then after baking cover with a damp cloth.

—Dull, firm crust will result if you add nothing on top.

—For a hard crust, brush with saltwater (¼ teaspoon to ¼ cup water) or put a pan of warm water in the bottom of the oven.

—For thick crusts, bake in glass, dull aluminum or dark tin bread pans.

Bake 20 Loaves at a Time

You can make 15 to 20 loaves at a time by baking them in large (46 oz.) juice cans. Let dough rise once. Grease can well. Put can half full of dough, let raise again not quite to the top rim, cover top with a piece of foil (save foil) and extend baking time by about 20 minutes or so. Saves time and electricity.

To clean cans—take bread out one can at a time. Immediately wipe the can out with a damp cloth for sparkly clean results—further sterilizing takes place during baking. Or 18 or so cans will fit in the bottom of an electric dishwasher.

"Note"— The joy of baking bread is learning to clean up immediately and expediently.

General Clean-Up Hints

—Put your flour bag on top of newspaper in case of spills. Then you can just roll up the newspaper to toss out afterwards.

—When making batter bread clean off the mix-master immediately as hardened dough is difficult to get off.

—Quickly clean up everything as you go, this makes breadmaking an easy, enjoyable task.

—When you make bread regularly, you can become so efficient that you can whip up a batch of bread in 20 minutes.

Easy Whole Wheat Bread (Economical)

2 Tbsp. (2 pkg.) yeast in ½ c. warm water with 1 tsp. honey (let stand about 10 minutes)
7 cups whole wheat flour
5 cups hot water from tap
2 Tbsp. salt
1/3 cup oil
7 more cups whole wheat flour

Sprinkle yeast in warm water with honey. Don't stir. Combine rest of ingredients in mixer except last 7 cups flour and yeast. Mix well. Add yeast and gradually add rest of flour. Follow directions for making home made bread. Bake at 350 degrees for 45 minutes. Makes 4 loaves.

Rich Flavored Whole Wheat Bread

Use above recipe but also add 2/3 cup molasses.

Honey Bread

Use above recipe but add 2/3 cup honey.

Vegetable Bread

Use above recipe. Put about 1 cup vegetables in blender; add some of recipe water to blender to make vegetable puree. Increase oil to 2/3 cup, and add extra flour at the end if necessary. Follow above directions. Use this same method to add other things to bread. See "Fancy-It-Up" section.

90-Minute Bread

They claim your bread is more nutritious if you let it rise twice, but if time doesn't permit, try this quick bread....Use Easy Whole Wheat Bread Recipe. Put all ingredients in bowl except last 7 cups flour. Mix all other ingredients in mixmaster until well blended. Gradually add 2 or 3 cups flour until dough is thick. Put rest of flour in deep bowl or plastic bucket to make a nest. Pour flour mixture in nest. Knead flour into dough until all flour is used up. Put dough on oiled table and knead until it feels elastic. Cut dough in four pieces. Put each piece in oiled pan without shaping loaf. Wet hand with water and flatten each loaf until all air is expelled. Cover with warm damp cloth and let rise in a warm place until almost double in bulk. Bake at 350 degrees for 45 minutes.

Batter Bread (No Knead)

Use Easy Whole Wheat recipe but instead of using 14 cups flour, just use 12 to 13 cups flour. Mix all ingredients in mixmaster. Pour batter into oiled pans and let rise in warm place until 1/3 in bulk. Bake at 425 degrees for 15 minutes, then at 350 degrees for remaining 25 to 30 minutes. Be aware that this bread has an open texture, and is more like cake.

Rich Man's Bread

2 Tablespoons yeast in ½ cup warm water with 1 teaspoon honey

1¾ cup warm milk
2 teaspoons salt
1/3 cup oil
1/3 cup honey or molasses
2 eggs
6 cups whole wheat flour (approximately)

Follow "Making Homemade Bread" directions. Bake 1 hour at 350 degrees. Makes 2 loaves.

Homemade Rolls

With an electric breadmixer, homemade rolls or bread dough is ready in 5 minutes—it's a marvelous appliance.

Basic Whole Wheat Sweet Dough

(for dinner rolls, or sweet bread and rolls)

2 packages (2 tablespoons) dry yeast
½ cup warm water
1 tablespoon honey
½ cup honey, molasses or any sugar
2 eggs, well beaten
1 teaspoon salt
½ cup oil or butter
1 cup warm milk
4-5 cups whole wheat flour

Add the tablespoon honey to warm water. Sprinkle yeast over sweet water. To well beaten eggs add rest of ingredients except flour. Stir well. Add yeast mixture. Add flour, stirring to a soft but sticky dough. Rest dough 10 minutes. Knead on floured board for about 10 minutes or until a soft pliable dough. Oil dough and let rise until double in bulk. Punch down. Let rise again as before. Punch down. Rest 10 or 15 minutes. Shape into rolls. Cover and let rise until almost double in bulk. Bake at 350 degrees for 15 to 20 minutes or until done. Don't overbake.

Rolls and Rolls and Rolls

Roll, fold, twist, or swirl dough to your liking. Let rise until light, 15 to 20 minutes. Heat oven to 400 degrees (mod. hot) Bake 12 to 15 minutes in lightly greased pan, muffin cups or on baking sheet. Serve hot, or cold.

Fluffy Waffles

½ cup warm water
1 T. honey or sugar
1 pkg. dry yeast

Combine above and let stand 5 minutes. Add:

1½ cups milk, buttermilk or yogurt
3 egg yolks
2/3 cup oil

Add:

1½ cups sifted whole wheat flour
1 t. salt
½ cup dry milk

Let rise, stirring down when double in bulk. Beat egg whites until stiff. Fold whites gently into batter. Bake in preheated waffle iron

Syrup

2 cups sugar
1 cup water
2 t. pure maple flavoring

Heat until sugar is dissolved. Ready to eat.

Pan Rolls Form dough into round smooth balls. 1/3 size desired. Place close together in a pan so they will bake together and have soft sides. If placed farther apart on baking sheet, they will bake with firm crusty sides.

Cloverleaf Rolls Form bits of dough into balls about 1" in diameter. Place 3 balls in each greased muffin cup. Brush with butter.

Crescents (Butterhorns) Roll dough about ¼" thick into a 12" circle. Spread with butter. Cut into 16 pie-shaped wedges. Beginning at wide edge, roll up. Place on baking sheet, point underneath.

Parker House Rolls Roll dough ¼" thick. Cut with biscuit cutter. Brush with melted butter. Make crease across each with back of knife and fold top half slightly over. Press edges together at middle crease. Place close together on baking sheet.

Twisted Shapes For twisted shapes, roll dough into an oblong 12" wide and a little less than ½" thick. Spread with soft butter. Fold ½ of dough over other half. Cut into strips ½" wide and 6" long.

Fan Fares Divide dough in half. Roll ⅛" thick into a square. Brush dough with melted butter. Cut into long strips 1½ inches wide. Stack 6 or 7 strips. Cut every 1½ inches with a string as shown. Place in buttered muffin tins with edges up. Let rise until double. Bake.

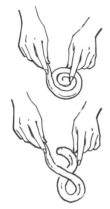

Snails or Coils hold one end of the strip down on baking sheet. Wind strip around and around. Tuck end under.

Figure 8's Hold one end of strip in one hand and twist other end, stretching it slightly until two ends are brought together, making figure 8.

CROSS AND TUCK

TUCK

Pretzel Rolls Divide dough into 2 or 3 equal pieces (depending on whether you want family or dinner-size rolls) Divide each piece into 12 pieces. Roll each piece into a pencil shaped 16-inch roll. Shape into pretzels. To do this pick up the end of each roll and cross, forming a circle as you do. Tuck the crossed ends under in the center of the circle. Place on greased baking sheets, about 2 inches apart. Keep the circle as wide as possible without stretching the dough. This will give the roll a distinctive pretzel shape.

Sugar Pecan Crisps

Use Basic Whole Wheat Sweet Dough and roll out in a large rectangle. Brush with melted butter, sprinkle with brown sugar and sprinkle with pecans (or other nuts). Roll like a cinnamon roll. Slice in 1" slices. Roll and flatten into 4" circles, rolling in brown sugar. Place on greased cookie sheet. Let rise. Bake at 375 degrees for about 10 minutes or until done.

Whole Wheat Rolls or Hamburger or Hot Dog Buns

Yield: 2 dozen

2 packages yeast in ¾ cup warm water
1 tablespoon honey
1/3 cup oil
¾ cup warm milk

1/3 cup brown sugar
2 eggs, well beaten
2 teaspoons salt
4 or 5 cups whole wheat flour

Mix 1 tablespoon honey with warm water, then sprinkle yeast over sweet water, and let stand 10 minutes. Mix together rest of ingredients except flour. Stir in yeast mixture. Add flour stirring thoroughly until you have a soft, but sticky dough. You get preferred results if dough is allowed to soften overnight in refrigerator, but if this isn't possible let dough rest 10 minutes, then knead. Oil kneaded dough and let rise in a bowl until double in bulk. Punch down and shape buns by taking pieces of golf ball sized dough, and flattening slightly. (Round for hamburger, oblong for hot dog) Cover pan of rolls and let rise until almost double. Bake at 375 degrees for 15 to 20 minutes. When cool slice buns lengthwise through the middle.

Whole Wheat Potato Rolls (No Knead)

DISSOLVE:
1 package (1 tablespoon) yeast
¼ cup warm water
COMBINE:
1 cup mashed potatoes (can use reconstituted instant)
1/3 cup brown sugar
½ cup oil
1 tablespoon salt
2 cups warm milk

Add yeast to above mixture, then add enough whole wheat flour to make stiff cookie-like dough. Mix well, cover and let rise until double. Beat down, cover and put in refrigerator. Chill 1 to 1½ hours—beat down if necessary. Spoon into muffin tins, ½ full. Let rise until double in size. Bake 375 degrees for 15 to 20 minutes.

Whole Wheat Cinnamon Rolls

Make Basic Whole Wheat Sweet Dough. Instead of shaping into rolls, roll dough ¼ inch thick into a long oblong piece. Spread flat oblong dough with soft butter. Then spread generously with brown sugar or honey and cinnamon. Roll up like a big jelly roll and slice in one-inch slices. Oil a cookie sheet with at least 1" sides and oil one pie plate. (A wonderful neighbor, Joyce Bock, brought us a pan of cinnamon rolls I've never forgotten—here is what she did.) Warm on stove 2/3 cup butter, 2/3 cup brown sugar and 2 tablespoons corn syrup or honey. Pour warm mixture into greased pans. Put cinnamon rolls on top of sauce, cover and let rise until almost double in bulk. Bake at 350 to 375 degrees for 20 minutes or until done. Don't overbake.

Take out of oven when done and turn hot pan and rolls upside down on large platter or waxed paper. Leave pan on rolls until sauce has basted rolls. Remove pan and eat hot or cold. (If you burn your mouth you have no will power.)

Bread Dough Cinnamon Rolls

Use some of your bread dough on "Breadmaking Day" and follow the procedure for whole wheat cinnamon rolls.

BREAD AND ROLLS—SUCCESS OR FAILURE

<u>Success is:</u>
<u>Appearance</u>

<u>Why Failure</u>
<u>Appearance</u>

−Well shaped and uniform in size. A uniform brown color−darker for batter bread.
−Regular bread is smooth with a tender crust−batter bread may have small bubbly surface.
−Sufficient volume. Uniform wheat color inside.

Failure- - - - - - - - - - - - - - - - - -Why?
Burned- - - - - Baked too long, Oven too hot.
Not brown enough- - - - Underbaked.
Cracks - - - - - Not enough kneading. Insufficient rising. Cooled too quickly.
Misshaped - - Improper shaping of loaf.
Insufficient Volume - - - Poor yeast or yeast killed. Needs more flour, and more rising.

<u>Texture</u>

<u>Texture</u>

No large air bubbles−
−<u>Rolls</u> - fine uniform thin cell walls.
−<u>Kneaded</u> - uniform, tiny, thin cell walls with even grain.
−<u>Batter</u> - medium cell walls with an open grain.

Failure- - - - - - - - - - - - - - - - - -Why?
Coarse - - - - - Oven too cool. Let rise too long. Needs more flour and more kneading.

Too heavy - - You had yeast growth.
Wrong type of flour.
Didn't rise long enough.
Too cool during rising.
Under mixed and under
kneaded.

Doughy - - - - Underbaked.

Crumb Feel

−Kneaded Bread and Rolls - moist
and fine with an elastic quality.
−Batter - moist, soft, and tender.

Crumb Feel

Failure - - - - - - - - - - - - - - - - - - -Why?

Streaked - - - Wrong flour, flour
added during shaping.
Poorly mixed and
kneaded. Improper
rising periods. Poor
quality yeast.

Dry,
　Crumbly - - Too much flour resulting
in too stiff dough.
Insufficient kneading.
Oven too cool.

Flavor

−It's soo good you drool all over
yourself.
−A pleasing mouth-watering aroma,
and nut-like taste.
−Now you know you're a pro.

Flavor

Failure - - - - - - - - - - - - - - - - - - Why?

Flat tasting - Not enough salt.

Too salty - - - You added too much
salt.

Yeasty - - - - -Too warm during rising
or too long of a rising
period.

Sour - - - - - - Too long rising period.
Sour attitude or poor
ingredients.

Bread, Rolls, Biscuit Storage

Never wrap, store or freeze homemade bread unless it's
cooled completely. Bread quickly develops mold if wrapped
while warm.

Fresh bread placed in a bag can be stored at room
temperature or in the refrigerator. Bread retains its freshness
longer at room temperature. If the weather is hot and humid or
if the bread has a moist texture, put in refrigerator to prevent
mold.

Bread may be stored if toasted or dried in open air or the sun. After totally dry, put in plastic bags, or containers with lids (like zwieback).

Frozen Dough, Bread, Rolls, Biscuits, Etc.

Baked products freeze more quickly with better results than doughs. But proper packaging for either is most essential to prevent freezer burn. Never thaw more than you can use quickly as all of these frozen foods dry out very fast.

Frozen Bread Dough

To freeze dough, make as usual, knead, and let rise until double in bulk. Punch down and knead slightly. Shape into small loaves and freeze. Most frozen foods should be thawed slowly, but NOT yeast bread dough. Put frozen dough in a warm 250 degrees oven for 40 to 45 minutes to thaw, then bake according to recipe. Commercial frozen dough—follow package directions. Again these breads dry out very easily, so use quickly.

Frozen Yeast Roll Dough

To freeze yeast rolls, follow Frozen Bread Dough instructions, then shape into rolls. Grease each roll totally, then freeze (2 or 3 hours) on open trays away from freezer walls. Bag as soon as frozen, not letting them sit on the open trays more than one full day. You may also just bag them, then freeze, but they will stick together if not properly separated. It will take 3 or 4 hours before these are thawed and ready to bake. To prepare for baking put frozen rolls in a warm place, cover with a damp cloth, and bake according to recipe directions when they are double in bulk. It is recommended that this roll dough not be frozen for more than about 10 days, but mine was and still worked well.

Frozen Biscuit Dough

Freeze biscuit dough the same as you would yeast roll dough but thaw in freezer wrapper for about one hour, then bake.

Frozen Partially Baked Doughs

Partially cooked breads and rolls may be baked without thawing.

Frozen Baked Bread or Rolls

Baked bread and rolls should be cooked thoroughly (2½ to 3 hours) before freezing, and make certain they are carefully wrapped, because they have excellent freezer life (some say 6 months, some claim up to one year. However, some flavor loss is determined after two or three months. I find that slicing bread before freezing has advantages. You can put the frozen slices right into your toaster. This also works well for frozen pancakes, french toast or sectioned waffles. This frozen sliced bread also thaws quickly at room temperature. To freeze commercial bread or rolls, for best results leave it in original wrapper and slip it into a plastic bag, then freeze.

About Whole Wheat Flour in Cakes, Cookies and Pastries

Hints

—Use water instead of milk for lighter cakes. Cookies you can add almost anything.

—Whole wheat flour in cakes, cookies, and pastries should always be sifted three times. Once before measuring and twice with other dry ingredients.

—If you have access to whole wheat pastry flour (health food store usually), it can be used in place of white flour, cup for cup.

—Whole wheat flour can be used in place of white flour always. Just remember to substitute ⅞ cup of sifted whole wheat flour for 1 cup sifted white flour. If substituting wheat flour for white in cake making you get excellent results if you add one more teaspoon of baking powder and one more egg. You have lighter cakes if you separate the eggs and beat the whites folding them in last.

—Never over-bake any cake, pastry, or cookie, they'll be dry and crumbly.

More Nutritious Icings

You may add some powdered milk to icings without sacrificing flavor.

—Use 1/3 cup powdered milk to 1½ cups powdered sugar.

—Use ¾ cup powdered milk to 2 cups powdered sugar.

(See my "Eating What Comes Naturally Cookbook" for Cakes, Cookies and Pastry recipes or use any recipe and follow the above hints)

How to Use
Various Wheat Doughs and Batters

Thin "Pour" Batter

Use 1 cup flour to 1 cup liquid and ½ teaspoon salt for a thin batter you can pour. This thin batter is possibly the most versatile dough. It can be used to make chips, cracker thins, crackers, scones, taco shells, cones, cold cereal, etc. (See thin batter recipes.)

Drop Batter

Use 1¾ cup to 2 cups flour to 1 cup liquid and ½ teaspoon salt for a drop batter or to spread. Drop batter can be used to make many of the foods as thin dough, but thin dough is much easier to work with.

Soft Dough

Use 2½ cups to 3 cups flour to 1 cup liquid and 1 teaspoon salt. Soft doughs are used to make breads, rolls, etc. (See recipes)

Stiff Dough

Use 3½ cups to 4 cups flour to 1 cup liquid and 1 teaspoon salt. Stiff doughs are used to make crackers, pizza crusts, bread sticks etc. (See recipes)

Basic Thin Batter to Pour

(Keep in refrigerator and use as needed)

3 cups flour
3 cups water
1½ teaspoons salt

Blend ingredients in blender or stir with spoon until free of lumps. This instant batter has many uses. It can be used to make chips, thins, cones, scones, crackers, taco shells, cold cereal, etc. Keep a large jar in your refrigerator to make these above instant foods. See following "thin batter" recipes.

Batter for Meat, Fish, Chicken, Vegetables, Etc.

Any foods to be deep fried are delicious if first dipped in "thin batter" then deep fried.

Delicious Instant (Fake) Potato Chips

A thin batter:
   1 cup whole wheat flour
   1 cup water
   ½ teaspoon salt

Put ingredients in blender or mix until free of lumps. Grease a large cookie sheet. Put tablespoons of dough around on cookie sheet or pour ½ cup of batter on entire sheet. If covering entire sheet roll batter around until surface is covered. Pour excess off at corner leaving a thin film. Season with plain, celery, onion, garlic, food powders or salts. Bake at 375 degrees for about 10 minutes. Bake several trays at a time. Remove already formed chips or break up to the size of chips.

Taco Chips

Same as above but season with taco seasoning.

Wheat Thins

Same as above, but leave heavier dough film on cookie sheet; don't pour excess off. Season to taste, and bake.

Garlic Thins

Same as wheat thins but season with garlic powder or salt.

Onion Thins

Same as wheat thins but season with onion powder or salt.

Whole Wheat Crackers No. 1

Pour "thin dough" on greased cookie sheet so it's about ⅛" thick. Sprinkle with plain, onion, celery, garlic, powders or crushed bacon bits, etc. Bake at 375 degrees to 400 degrees for 10 or so minutes. Cut while hot.

Cracker Delights (No. 1 variation)

Put "thin dough" in a squirt bottle and slowly squirt designs, characters, and fun things on a greased or teflon cookie sheet. Sprinkle with plain, onion, celery, garlic, powders, etc. Bake at 375 degrees from 8 to 10 minutes. Eat as is or decorate.

Whole Wheat Crackers No. 2

Take some of your wheat bread dough and add extra flour until it's absolutely stiff. Roll out until about ⅛ inch thick, sprinkle with food powders or salt. Cut dough to desired cracker size. Bake at 325 degrees for 15 to 18 minutes, or until done.

Ice Cream Cones

Add honey to taste to "thin batter" and pour ½ cup batter (or use ⅛ inch thick rolled sweetened stiff dough) onto a large greased or teflon cookie sheet so entire surface is covered. Pour excess off at corner. Bake at 375 degrees for 7 or 8 minutes. Remove from oven and shape into cones. Pinch the bottom and seams to seal. Stand on end or roll around a small thin cardboard cone and bake for 1 or 2 minutes more. Cool.

If you overbake, put over steam to shape cones.

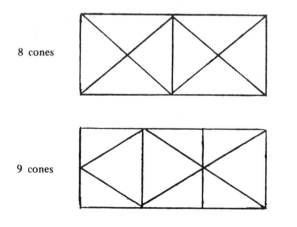

8 cones

9 cones

For 8 cones cut dough into triangles on cookie sheet or for 9 smaller cones cut as shown.

The Breakfast Cereal Racket

Commercial breakfast cereals are an extremely poor buy for your nutritional dollar. Robert B. Choate, Jr., a former government advisor on hunger, on July 24, 1970 speaking before the Consumers Sub-committee of the Senate Commerce Committee reported, "The poor nutritional content of 40 leading breakfast cereals is so low that they are almost a threat of *empty calories.* And speaking as a private citizen Mr. Choate charged that "for a budget-conscious family, they are a bad nutrient investment for the dollar," because most commercial cereals "fatten but do little to prevent malnutrition." He also pointed out that children are not being given proper nutritional knowledge and they are "being programmed to demand sugar and sweetness in every food."

Many commercial cereals contain more sugar than grain and nutritional researchers have cited experiments that the high carbohydrate in *refined* white flour, corn flakes, wheat flakes, oatmeal, and white rice products caused tooth decay in experimental animals. These type cereals made with natural grains *reduced* tooth decay drastically.[1]

The wonderful grains are shot through guns, so 100 million steam explosions occur in ever kernal. They are shredded, crinkled puffed and popped at extremely high heats (almost 400 degrees F.), and put in colorful boxes with rewarding box tops, prizes and pictures of athletes to lure their best consumer—the children.

Presweetened Cereals Could Dig Small Graves

A major attack is being brought against sugar-coated breakfast cereals as being dangerous to health. The Center for

Science in the Public Interest of Washington D.C. charged that these cereals should carry a health warning similar to the warning on cigarette packages.

Dr. Michael Jacobson, codirector of the center declared that "some of these cereals which are so attractive to children can be as much a health hazard as smoking. The extremely high sugar content of some pre-sweetened cereals contributes to tooth decay, obesity, heart disease, diabetes, and other health problems."[2]

Do you parents realize that some popular cereals have as much as 50 percent sugar? This means for a 4 oz. portion, your children could be consuming 18 teaspoons of sugar. Shocking isn't it? Especially when their little bodies are begging for some nourishment.

Most Cereals Should Have a Health Warning

Any cereal containing more than 10 percent sugar, Dr. Jacobsen charges, should have a health warning....One head of a major cereal company retorted, "The amount of sugar eaten by children in pre-sweetened cereals is insignificant." It seems to me if cereal companies pretend to be that uninformed concerning nutrition, they certainly shouldn't be feeding our children, especially the most important meal of the day. They are tampering with our children's health to make the almighty dollar—$800 million of them a year.

Sugar Content of Leading Cereals

According to the Center for Science in the Public Interest, these cereals contain the following percentages of sugar:

King Vitamin	50	Corn Chex	14
Cocoa Pebbles	44	Life	14
Fruity Pebbles	44	Product 19	12
Super Sugar Crisp	43	Total	11
Sir Grapefellow	40	Concentrate	11
Post Alpha-Bits	40	Wheaties	11
Cocoa Krispies	38	Special K	9
Captain Crunch	37	Corn Flakes	7
Fruit Loops	35	Rice Krispies	7
Super Sugar Corn Chex	33	Post Toasties	7
Mr. Wonderful Surprise	29	Raisen Bran	6
Sugar Frosted Flakes	29	Wheat Chex	6
Post Oat Flakes	20	Rice Chex	5
100% Natural	19	Cheerios	4

Many leading nutritionists warn that most commercial breakfast cereals are extremely poor food buys. Do your family and your budget a favor; make your own. Homemade cereal costs 1 or 2 cents a bowl, and is highly nutritious.

Homemade Cereals Verses Commercial Brand X

It costs up to one dollar per pound for prepared cereals in the stores. About 10 cents or less a pound if you use homemade wheat cereal in your home.

—5 pounds of cracked wheat = 15 cups or 85 to 90 servings

—1 cup of cracked wheat, after 1 hour cooking = 6 servings

—you pay 10 times as much for prepared cereal as you do for cooked cracked wheat cereal.

—add any other grains to wheat to make delicious, nutritious cereals.

Wheat or Other Grain Cereals

Whole Wheat or Any Grain

1 cup clean whole wheat
2 cups water
salt to taste just before serving

Place wheat and water in casserole dish (1 to 2 quart capacity). Place casserole, without a lid, on a perforated can or adapter ring of a steamer, or use the deep well in an electric range, placing casserole dish on adjustable trivet. Place water in bottom of steamer or deep well to within 1 inch of adapter ring or trivet. The steamer or deep well should have a tightfitting lid but the casserole with wheat in it is always uncovered. Bring water in bottom of pan to full rolling boil and boil for about 15 minutes. Reduce heat to low or simmer. Steam for 10 to 12 hours or overnight. This recipe makes 8 servings. Keep unused portion in refrigerator and reheat just before serving. (A crock pot is excellent for this.)

Cracked Wheat - or Any Grains Cereal

1 cup cracked wheat
3 cups hot water (2½ for quick method)
½ teaspoon salt—add just before serving.

Quick Method 1: Put cracked wheat in pan. Gradually add 1 cup hot water, stirring to a paste. Add rest of water gradually, stirring, and bring to a boil. Add lid, remove from heat. Let sit for 20 minutes without lifting lid. Add salt and serve.

Method 2: Cook in double boiler for 1 hour or more.

Method 3: Start in double boiler or crock pot at night and cook for 30 minutes. Put on lid and put aside until morning. (Avoid this method in hot climates—bacteria problem). The longer it cooks the more cereal you get.

Whole Wheat - or Any Other Grain Flour Cereal

    1 cup whole wheat flour
    2 cups hot water
    ½ teaspoon salt—add just before serving

Follow "quick method" for instructions. You may sprinkle ¼ cup nuts, raisins, dates, or figs on top each dish homemade cereal for a delicious treat.

Homemade Wheat Flakes

Mix together:
    3 cups milk
    2 tablespoons honey
Add and mix thoroughly:
    4 cups whole wheat flour
    1 teaspoon soda (optional)
    1 cup (not packed) brown sugar
    1 teaspoon salt

Beat until smooth. Spread ⅛ to ¼ inch on 2 or 3 cookie sheets. Sometimes edges burn, so cover with foil. Bake at 350 degrees for 35 to 45 minutes or until golden crisp. Cool thoroughly, then break up into flakes. Store in air-tight container. Makes up to 6 cups cold cereal.

Grand Ola (breakfast food)

    5 cups oatmeal
    1 cup almonds (or other nuts)
    ¾ cup sesame seeds
    1 cup sunflower seeds
    1 cup shredded coconut
    1 cup soy flour
    1 cup powdered milk
    1 cup honey
    1 cup vegetable oil

Warm wet ingredients and mix with dry ingredients. Spread on 2 baking sheets. Bake 300 degrees for 20 to 25 minutes or longer. Watch carefully and stir often, as it burns easily. Bake until light brown. Serve with milk for breakfast. Good as a snack. Refrigerate.

Healthy Granola Cereal Mix

4 cups rolled oats uncooked
½ cup grated coconut
1/3 cup wheat germ
1/3 cup brown sugar
1/3 cup vegetable oil
1/3 cup honey
1/3 cup sunflower seeds
1 cup any kind of nuts

Combine all ingredients, in large bowl and mix well. Bake on ungreased pan at 350 degrees for 20 to 30 minutes. Stir often to keep it browning evenly. Store in tight container. Serve with milk. Raisins may be added after it is cooked. Cinnamon or other flavorings may be added.

Part 4

Our

Remade

Meats

Section I

Meat—Follow God's Direction

When in doubt as to what we should eat, why not consult the dietary laws given us by the "Great Scholar." He gave us explicit instructions for eating, especially in the meat department.

Here's how the Bible instructs us in Leviticus, Chapter 11, and Deuteronomy 14, concerning meats we should or should not eat.

Leviticus, Chapter 11:1-12.

And the Lord spake unto Moses and to Aaron, saying unto them,

Speak unto the children of Israel, saying, These are the beasts which ye shall eat among all the beasts that are on the earth.

Whatsoever parteth the hoof, and is clovenfooted, and cheweth the cud, among the beasts, that shall ye eat.

Nevertheless these shall ye not eat of them that chew the cud, or of them that divide the hoof; as the camel, because he cheweth the cud, but divideth not the hoof; he is unclean to you.

And the hare, because he cheweth the cud, but divideth not the hoof, he is unclean unto you.

And the swine (pig) though he divide the hoof, and be clovenfooted, yet he cheweth not the cud; he is unclean to you.

Of their flesh shall ye not eat, and their carcass shall ye not touch; they are unclean to you.

These shall ye eat of all that are in the waters; whatever hath fins and scales in the waters, in the seas, and in the rivers, them shall ye eat.

And all that have not fins and scales in the seas, and in the rivers, of all that move in the waters, and of any living thing which is in the waters, they shall be an abomination unto you.

They shall be even an abomination unto you; ye shall not eat of their flesh, but ye shall have their carcasses in abomination.

Whatsoever hath no fins nor scales in the waters, that shall be an abomination unto you.

Author Elmer A. Josephson points out that:

The clean animals that chew the cud have a divided hoof such as the ox, sheep, goat, deer, cow, steer, buffalo, etc., because of the sacculated condition of the alimentary canal and secondary cud receptacle, have practically three stomachs as refining agencies and cleansing laboratories, for the purifying of their food. This cleanses their systems of all poisonous and deleterious matter. It takes their food over twenty-four hours to be turned into flesh, which flesh even the pre-Mosiac law said was clean.[1] (See About Pork)

Even though we have been directed to eat some of the above meats, today's commercial practices of meat raising and handling present some real problems for us, the consumer.

Modern Meat—The Man Killer

Senator Walter F. Mondale of Minnesota who worked to get the 1967 Wholesome Meat Law said:

"Modern science has developed and continues to develop new wonder chemicals—additives, preservatives and colorations—which can prevent the consumer from using the normal smell and sight tests to determine spoilage or deterioration....Consumers have no chance at all to determine the safety of the meat they buy."

Our Beef About Beef

Of all the foods we eat, commercial meat has to be the most potentially harmful. If at all possible, search out reputable sources that raise their beef with old-fashioned natural methods. It's worth all your efforts. Here's why:

Beef used to be animals that were matured slowly. It used to take several years to get the animals ready for the butcher. Animals exercised; their countenance was that of a lean, strong appearance. When butchered, their fat was soft, largely unsaturated, and yellow in color.

Synthetic Meats

Today our meat is somewhat synthetic, because our animals are fed a lot of synthetic feed. Cheap urea-carbohydrate formulas are fed to livestock, instead of natural high protein foods.[2]

Artificial roughage pellets are made from food-grade plastic for cattle on high-concentrate or all-grain rations. Ground-up newspapers, mixed with molasses have been fed to cattle at Pennsylvania State University. Feathers have also been used. Treated wood has been used as a supplement in animal food at the College of Agriculture at Missouri.[3]

Drug Addicted Cattle

Stilbestrol, a synthetic drug, used to increase weight rapidly, was used in up to 85 percent of beef cattle. It's also used for sheep. Stilbestrol is labeled by scientists as "biological dynamite." It also causes leukemia and cysts in animals. And breast cancer, fibroid tumors, and excessive menstrual bleeding in women, sterility and impotence in men, and arrested growth in children."[4] Not to mention that almost 98 percent of all animal feeds contain additives.

An entire book could be written on what is done to the meat sitting on our tables, but space will permit only a small eye opener to these facts. . .

Medicine in Animal Feed

It is also estimated that up to $60 million worth of antibiotics are used in this country on animal feed crops. In the *Health Bulletin,* "Drugs in Meat Among Problems of Food Industry," Dr. Hubert S. Goldberg warns that drugs interfere with phsysicians' attempts to cure infections using these antibiotics. Other experts claim this overuse of antibiotics in animals could cause an epidemic or resistance to these drugs in treating human infections.

Cooking won't destroy antibiotic deposits or most drug residues. We're eating them right along with our meat. Continued eating of these may result in hardening of the arteries and associated heart disease.[5]

Our meat animals are given tranquilizers, female hormones (progesterone and estrogen), pesticides (DDT) and you name it. We should have some guarantee that we're getting safe, healthful food.

Dangerous Meat—Here's More Proof!

Dr. Oscar Sussman, D.V.M., M.P.H., President of the New Jersey Public Health Association, warned in the American Public Health Association's *Nation's Health* that the American Public Health Association intends to go to court unless the government makes public the possible hazards still contained in "U.S. Inspected" meat. He said APHA wants labeling on packages of meat, similar to the warnings of cigarette packages.

Meat Packing Plant Filth

However, there are other problems: many people were horrified at the condition of meat plants in Upton Sinclair's book, *The Jungle,* where filthy practices occurred in handling our meat. Spot checks around the country tell us these abominable conditions still exist.

What Can Be Done?

Raise your own beef if possible, or again, search for a reputable source. When the meat manufacturers are aware that we know what's taking place, hopefully the pressure will bring about some positive changes. Also never eat meat that isn't well cooked, as rare commercial meats could be a health hazard.

The Hamburger Hoax

Dr. M. R. Clarkson said, "We can't depend on laboratory analysis of samples to protect consumers against unfit or adulterated meat and poultry products. It is impossible to detect them—even microscopically—when mixtures have been chopped or blended or cooked."[6]

So it is with hamburger—ground meat readily invites rapid bacteria growth. Broken tissues and cell fluids mix with bacteria to stimulate multiplication of micro-organisms.

Hamburger may have such additives as cochineal (has caused death), coal-tar colors (cancerous), benzoate of soda and sodium nitrate (has proven to cause cancer). Sodium sulfite, a harmful additive often used by restaurants, cafeterias, etc., may be used to redden and disguise the offensive odors of deteriorating meat to make it look fresh. This meat, if not thoroughly cooked, can cause serious damage to the digestive system and other organs.[7] Medical Tribune reported that sodium nicotinate is also used to redden meat, and is illegal in Chicago and New York City, but some states still allow it.[8]

Where's the Meat?

Consumer Union pointed out that hamburger should only contain beef, pork and veal. But in testing the Union found some samples contained horse and kangaroo meat. The union also found such additions as; skeletal muscle, lung, pancreas, muscles of lips, snouts, and in further testing found testicular tissue of a bull ground into a sample.[9]

Some companies have even gone so far as to use up to 90 percent fat, added blood to stain the meat and sell it as hamburger.[10]

Be aware that chopped meats can contain a lot of filth. "Samples of ground hamburger meat were found at various times grossly contaminated with substances such as unfit meat, mold growth, rodent hair, insects, and manure-type soil."[11]

Buying Hamburger

When buying hamburger you just don't know what you're getting, so I'd suggest grinding your own or watching a reputable butcher grind it. It's advisable to buy a meat grinder as it could pay for itself in a short time as you could buy cheaper cuts of meat, grind them and know what you are getting. Some cuts of meats are much cheaper than hamburger so there is a considerable savings.

Also be aware that this meat should be bright red in color. If it's pink, there's too much fat; if it's dull red or brownish, it's not fresh.

Poor Porky Pig

(This is extremely unappetizing information—Don't read this before or just after eating.)

Leviticus, Chapter 11, Verses 7 and 8, the Lord said:

And the swine (pig) though he divideth the hoof, and be clovenfooted, yet he cheweth not the cud; he is unclean to you.
Of their flesh shall ye not eat, and their carcass shall ye not touch; they are unclean to you.

Since most of us ignore these wise biblical dietary laws, let me encourage you in eating pork, for maximum protection and health, to search out farmers who don't "slop" their hogs by feeding them garbage, etc. Search out reputable sources for pork that have grain or corn fed hogs and give them balanced diets.

Nature's Scavengers

Nature created animals known as the "scavengers" of the earth. Such animals are necessary to keep the filth off the earth. The pig is a scavenger we have domesticated. He will eat absolutely anything, regardless of condition: rotten, dead, decayed, diseased, filthy food is the common diet of most pigs, and his body has no cleaning system for purifying this food.

"The swine's (hog) anatomy, as a supplement to his bad appetite (eating any putrid thing he finds), has but one poorly constructed stomach arrangement, and very limited excretory organs generally. Consequently, in about four hours after he has eaten his polluted swill and other putrid and offensive matter, man may eat the same, second-handed off the ribs of the pig...."

Mr. John Johnson of Williams, Iowa, a farmer says, "The swine in Iowa are principally fed on corn, but they will eat anything we give them. If anything dies, we throw it to the hogs. I have actually seen hogs chewing on the cancer of other hogs and these are shipped to market...."[12]

"If swine are raised in a lot with other animals such as the horse, the cow, etc., they will eat and drink the very refuse of animals."

The Poisoned Pig

Most pigs actually have "running sores" under their hooves. Lift the front hoof of a hog and with just a little pressure you will find greenish matter oozing out from between his "toes." This is one outlet for the various deadly poisons he takes into his body. Sometimes this artery becomes stopped up, the poison backs up and greenish growths are formed in various parts of his body.

An employee of a meat packing plant confirmed that he had worked only a few days in a meat packing plant and had seen hogs come down the line with these big greenish growths. "We were instructed to just trim them off and when the meat inspector came he put his stamp on them." Such statements have been made repeatedly by others who have worked in meat packing plants.[13] Ugh!

Successful Farming Journal emphasized that "Disease problems are a hazard with hogs, but offsetting that is the fact that hogs are easier to buy and sell than cattle.[14]

Many people who have garbage routes raise commercial hogs. The garbage that is rotted, infested with deadly disease and maggots, could be indirectly sitting on your plate as a pork chop.

You say this isn't possible? Let me assure you that this material is not dreamed up to cause alarm. This is actually what takes place. Search out grain and corn fed pigs, so you can be guaranteed unpolluted meat.

What About Sausage?

Pork in itself can have definite health hazards, but sausage has added problems. In one food report, June 1970, "Sausage and Spice (and things not so nice)" it was reported that an unbelievable amount of filth comes into the sausage through the spices, and the FDA allows a certain level of filth in many foods, including spices. (See spices). In many court cases they have ruled that the presence of a minimal amount of filth may be insufficient grounds for condemnation. "The FDA keeps its filth tolerances a secret."

Some food tests, August 1968, reported finding insect fragments, insect larvae, rodent hairs, and other kinds of unappealing extraneous matter in 12.5 percent of the samples of Federally inspected sausage tested for such impurities.

Kosher Means Clean?

Are you confident about the meat plants around the country? *New York Times* reported on a *federally inspected kosher sausage firm* examined in February, 1968. Another New York inspector found almost seventy-five violations. Among them:

"Evidence of rats was everywhere, even where meat was being handled...and there was a Federal Inspector on the premises."
"The worm gears in the meat grinder were rusty and caked with bits of old fat and meat. Paint was scaling off the equipment and falling into the hot dog mixtures. Fresh meat was being stored in rusty tubs."[15]

If You Eat Sausage—Make Your Own!
Recipes for Sausage Making

Pork Sausage

2 pounds clean ground pork
2 teaspoons salt
1 2/3 teaspoons sage
1 teaspoon black pepper
1/4 teaspoon ground cloves
1 teaspoon honey

Directions below...

Porky Beef

1 pound clean, lean ground pork
1 pound lean ground beef
1/2 pound ground fat pork
1 tablespoon salt
1 teaspoon black pepper
2 1/4 teaspoons sage
3/8 teaspoon ground cloves.

Directions below...

Spicy Spanish Sausage

  2 pounds clean fatty pork
  3 tablespoons dry onions
  1 clove minced garlic
  2 teaspoons salt
  1 teaspoon black pepper
  ½ teaspoon ground chili pepper (dried)
  1¼ teaspoon paprika

Directions for Sausage Making

Use ground meat or grind once in ¼ inch sieve. Mix in spices thoroughly. Stuff casings (synthetic or animal). Cook, submerged in hot water over very low heat on top of stove, until water evaporates (at least an hour). Add more water if necessary. When casing splits, sausage is done. Refrigerate immediately and eat within about 4 days. Cook again before eating.

No. 1—Mix recipe meats, seasonings and spices together. Blend thoroughly, leaving no unmixed spots.

No. 2—Fill the stuffer with the uncooked sausage.

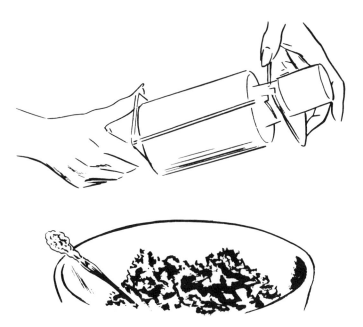

No. 3—Close the stuffer to pack the meat tightly.

No. 4—Animal casings have to be soaked in water. Soak while sausage is being made. (Synthetic casings do not require soaking.) Tie one end tightly, to prevent meat from oozing out.

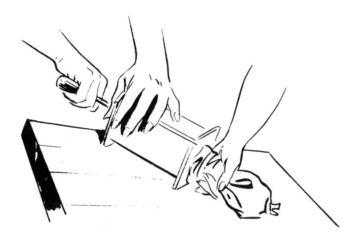

No. 5—It's easier if a helper holds the casing, while you force the meat into the casing.

No. 6—Tie the end of the casing when you have finished.

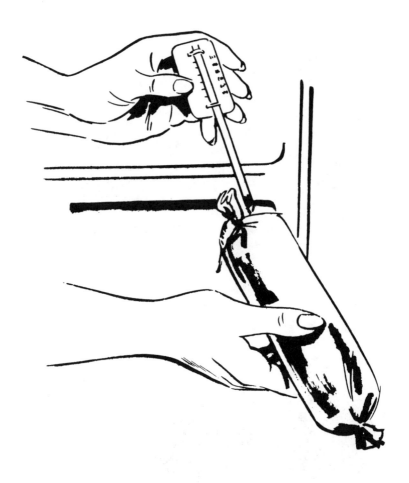

No. 7—Insert a meat thermometer into the end of the sausage. When it registers 160 degrees in the center, it is done.

The Startling Facts About Processed Meats

(Frankfurters, Bologne, Lunch Meats and other Sausage Meats)

Ralph Nader warns us "Don't Eat That Dog" in an informative article in *The New Republic.* He reports: The frankfurter is: fraud, low nutritional value and health hazards abound, in varying degrees, in most of the 15 billion franks sold annually. The hot dog is offering less nutrition and more fat and added water than its predecessor did 35 years ago during the depression.[16] (Fat content is 30 percent or more.)

The hot dog is a very low protein food—mostly fat fillers and chemicals.

Nader also points out that usually the worst meat goes into cooked sausage products, such as hot dogs. They put the beef portions of beef cattle into frankfurters that could not be sold undisguised. Federal law allows the inclusion of esophagi, lips, snouts, ears and other edible offal, and skeletal muscle tissue. The 1967 congressional hearings produced evidence of the use of '4D' animals (dead, dying, diseased and disabled) in these processed meats.[17] Yuk!

Hot Dogs—The $10 a Pound Protein

Time Magazine emphasized: "To Nader, the ABM and the smart bomb are scarcely more lethal than a chain of processed sausages."

Time points out that hot dogs are loaded with additives, including sodium nitrate, sodium acid pyrophosphate and glucona-delta-lactone. Without such chemicals, the hot dog would lose its pink blush and turn the color of unwashed sneakers. There can also be occasional insect parts and rodent hairs. What protein remains comes to more than $10 a pound. For that you could buy 4 pounds of filet mignon.[18]

The manufacturers defend the frankfurter by saying it has "fewer chemicals than in most cereals, mustard, mayonnaise or oleo margarine."[19]

The inspection tests of frankfurters found 40 percent of favorite brands to have bacteria counts of over 10 million per gram; a level where spoilage and putrification sets in. Some packages tested actually had 140 million bacteria per gram.

Read the labels of foods such as frankfurters, bologne, cold meats, chopped meats, etc., they all contain sodium nitrate and is supposed to inhibit bacteria growth, but it's chief role is to keep the meat a reddish color. Evidence says that nitrates cause cancer.

Nitrites combine with certain substances called amines in food and the human body to form nitrosamines. Dr. William Lyinsky of the Atomic Energy Commission's Oak Ridge National Laboratories, a cancer researcher, points out that evidence is accumulating about the formation of nitrosamines from nitrates and secondary or tertiary amines both in food and in vivo, which suggests that nitrosamines formed in this way are a cause of cancer.[20]

Dr. Lyinsky testified that "Nitrosamines...seem to be most effective in eliciting tumors when they are applied in small doses over a long period of time."

Dr. Samuel Epstein, a respected toxicologist at Cleveland's Case Western Reserve University calls nitrosamines "one of the major public issues of our time."

Do you love frankfurters and cold cuts? They can be unhealthy foods—make them yourself.

Other Homemade Sausage Meats

—You Know It's Good

(Frankfurters, Bologne, Salami, Cold Meats, etc.)

Sausage may be all beef, all pork, or a combination of these or any ground meats with spices. Meats may be fresh or cooked, partially cooked or thoroughly cooked, dry or partially dry or even smoked. There are 200 plus varieties of sausage and they can cover a wide variety of foods: frankfurters, bologne, salami, cold meats; you name it. Make your own at home, then you know what you're eating.

Homemade Cold Cuts—Seasoned to Suit You

Be aware that homemade lunch meat will not be exactly like the commercial product, but you have control of what goes into it. The texture will not be as firm or smooth. It will slice differently, and the color will not be as pink even when food coloring is added, but it's reassuring to know it's not loaded with nitrates and possibly diseased animals. It won't taste the same, but you don't want it to; season to your liking. It can be delicious, so don't be afraid to try it. It's simple to make.

There are three basic types of cold meats:

1. *Basic Blend Emulsion*—Ground meat is liquified in a blender to form an emulsion. This is the method for basic bologne or frankfurters. You may add spices, seasonings, extenders, vegetables, etc., to your taste. Commercially, a few types are: regular bologne or Leona style, pickle, pimento and olive loaf, italian, vegetable, macaroni and cheese, etc.

2. *Basic Blend with Added Meat*—This is the above basic blend with added ground or chunk meat. A few of the commercial names are: salami, luncheon, luxury, Dutch, spiced luncheon loaf, Proschke, etc.

3. *Ground Method*—This method has no emulsion. Ground meat is used and larger meat pieces may be added if desired. A few commercial types are: fresh Polish, summer, Kosher or all beef sausage; cooked salami (cotto salami); Lebanon Bologne, minced luncheon, tongue, cheese, ham, beef, or pork loaves—Precook all additional ingredients before adding to give variety.

Equipment Needed (Buy good equipment, it's worth the investment)

1. *Meat thermometer*—Invest in a good one because you need accurate readings between 140 and 160 degrees F. With proper care it will last for years.
2. *Blender*—Necessary to emulsify the meat. It must be able to liquefy the meat and have a motor of 350 watts or more.
3. *Loaf Pans*—If you're going to invest in loaf pans, the non-stick give better results because of even heat distribution. Get one or two pound size. Others will work, however.
4. *What about Casings?* You don't need these, but in using them, you'll be more pleased with the results. Synthetic casings are preferred as they help prevent meat from spoil-

ing. These may be purchased locally in some areas or *see mail order address below.** For cold cuts get the 6-inch by 20-inch. These can be cut to desired lengths. Animal casings may be used in sausage making, but be sure they are thoroughly cleaned—soak for several minutes in warm water and rinse out immediatley before using. *Beef casings*—too tough for sausage making. *Standard Hog casings*—used for country style or large link sausage. *Pork casings*—Use as desired, but clean thoroughly. *Sheep casings*—good for small link sausage. Medium links or franks may be made with medium sheep or small hog casings.

5. *Other equipment*—A sturdy rubber spatula, measuring spoons, large measuring cup, large wooden spoon and large sturdy mixing bowl.

6. *Additional equipment* (optional)—An electric meat slicer is excellent. However, an electric knife is better than a regular knife for slicing; a sausage stuffer gives better results *(hardware store or see below).** It is handy and inexpensive.

Variety for Cold Cuts Ingredients

You need four basic ingredients for homemade lunch meats: meat, extenders, seasonings, and coloring (optional).

Meat—Beef, pork, veal, and why not wild meats? Never use more than 20 to 25 percent fat—even less. Hamburger not advised (too fatty), so use ground round, chuck, etc. Grind meat through 1/8 inch sieve if not already ground.

Extenders—Popular choices for economy and top nutrition are powdered milk or ground soya (ground, unseasoned, roasted soybeans—soak them, roast them and put them in a blender at home if available, 1/2 cup at a time).

Seasonings and Color—Season to please your palate. Red food coloring (grocery store) may be added. —But go easy Mama as the pink commercial color is from preservatives and we "ain't addin' em." Homemade cold cuts are brownish in color.

---

*Synthetic Casings—Wine Merchant Limited, 11108 W. Blue Mound Road, Milwaukee, WI 53226. Write for Price and information.

* *Consumer Guide* recommends a sausage stuffer ordered by mail from E. R. Wagner Co., Hustesford, Wis. 53034. Stock No. 90951. They claim excellent performance and low cost.

Here's How You Do It!

(Some recipes may vary slightly)

1. Buy ground meats or run meat through a ⅛ inch sieve in a meat grinder.
2. Place ¼ cup (no more) of meat in blender and turn to "liquefying speed." (NEVER add meat while blender is on.)
3. Quickly add small amounts of ice water to emulsify. Add tiny amounts until mixture looks thick, like peanut butter. (Add food coloring here if desired.)
4. Stop blender. Fold mixture with spatula. Blend again for total emulsion.
5. Remove emulsified meat, and *repeat the same procedure* until all other meat is emulsified.
6. Put all emulsified meat into a large mixing bowl and add spices. *Mix thoroughly* with a wooden spoon. Unmixed "meat spots" will ruin the meat so mix totally and thoroughly.
7. Put meat mixture into one or two loaf pans or casing (tie end of casing). Place filled casing into a tight fitting loaf pan (eliminates air bubbles). Insert meat thermometer through the center (for casings at the end of the loaf.)
8. Put loaf pans in another pan that is partially filled with hot water. Keep water at 160 to 162 degrees on top of stove or bake in a 260 degrees oven for 2 to 3 hours or until meat thermometer registers 160 to 162 degrees.
9. Remove meat from pan and cool at room temperature. Refrigerate. Slice and serve when desired as it doesn't require aging.

Storing Your Cold Cuts

This lunch meat must be kept in the refrigerator and should be used within two weeks. It may also be frozen—whole or sliced.

Lunch Meat Recipes

Leona Style Bologne (or franks)

3 pounds ground beef
2 pounds ground pork
1 cup dry powdered milk
1 synthetic casing (medium sheep casing for franks)
¼ ounce liquid smoke (optional)

3½ tablespoons salt
1½ teaspoons honey
1 tablespoon plus ½ teaspoon white pepper (white pepper
is much milder than black. If using black, use less.)
1¼ teaspoons sage
1½ teaspoons cardamon
1½ teaspoons coriander
¾ teaspoon alspice
¾ teaspoon mace
Red food coloring to desired color (optional)

*Buy ground meat or grind with ⅛ inch sieve. Place ¼ cup
(no more) ground meats in blender and emulsify. Add ice water
and coloring until thick paste. Repeat until all meat is ground.
Put in bowl and add dry milk and spices. Important: mix meat,
dry milk and spices very thoroughly. Stuff meat into casings (or
pan) with large spoon or stuffer. Put in meat thermometer.
Force casing into a very tight fitting pan (if pan is too long, put
metal lids, etc. to form a snug fit). Place pan in another pan of
water in 260 degrees oven or a constant 160-162 degrees water
double boiler. It's done when thermometer registers 160-162
degrees. Put in cold (ice) water to quick cool (about 15
minutes). Then place at room temperature until thermometer
registers 100 degrees or a little less. Refrigerate. Slice and
Serve.*

Pimiento and Pickle Lunch Meat

3 pounds ground beef
2 pounds ground pork
1 cup dry powdered milk
1 cup soya flour
½ cup pickle relish
2½ ounces dices pimientos
1½ tablespoons white pepper or less black pepper
2 tablespoons salt
1 tablespoon honey
¾ teaspoon ginger
Follow directions for Leona Bologne.

Country Style Bologne

Exact ingredients for Leona Bologne except increase
powdered milk to 2 cups. DO NOT emulsify meat, just mix
ground meats thoroughly with rest of ingredients and follow

rest of Leona Bologne directions. Cook to 150 degrees internal temperature.

Homemade Corned Beef

Since commercial corned beef is loaded with nitrates and saltpeter (a harmful additive) add your own corny touch. This will not be the same color as commercial corned beef; 1½ teaspoons saltpeter adds color, plus health problems. You decide.

For corning combine:

4 quarts hot water
2 cups coarse salt
¼ cup sugar
2 tablespoons mixed whole spice

Cool and pour over a 5 pound piece of beef brisket or tongue in an enameled pot or large stone jar. Add 3 cloves garlic. Put a weight on meat to keep submerged. Cure this in refrigerator for three weeks. Turn meat every 4 or 5 days.

After three weeks, rinse under running water to remove brine. Cover with boiling water and simmer 4 or more hours, or until fork goes easily to center. Serve with horseradish.

Section V

Our Poor Poultry

In raising your own chickens there is double benefit. You get wonderful fresh eggs (see egg section). You also have access to wholesome fresh poultry meat.

Poultry used to be able to roam and scratch in large unsprayed open fields where they lived on good old mother earth, with plenty of sunshine and unpolluted air. Today's chickens don't have this privilege. They are fed cheap feed, aspirin and stilbesterol among many other harmful feeds. Stilbesterol, again, is a fattening agent (so is aspirin)—in fact a scientific witness testifying before the Delany Committee claims that the consumer "pays protein prices for contaminated fat....Minks fed such stilbesterol treated chicken necks become sterile....Even in small amounts it can change the reproductive tract." Canada banned the use of stilbesterol discovering that women who had been through the menopause, started to menstruate again after eating the livers of stilbesterol-treated fowl. Small amounts of this hormone sterilized men who are now only marginally fertile.[21]

Widespread Chicken Cancer

Today's poultry are in such crowded, unbelievable conditions that disease is rampant. Standards are so low that the Surgeon General has warned "Over 90 percent of chickens from most flocks in this country and abroad are infected with leukosis viruses, even though a much smaller percentage develop overt neoplasms (tumors)."[22]

Poultry Inspection Practices

A few years ago, the U.S.D.A.'s policy was to discard the whole chicken if any part of the bird showed signs of leukosis.

The poultry industry considered this too severe and suggested a lowering of the standards for condemning birds. A new panel reviewed the problem and suggested that chickens bearing cancer virus be allowed on the market if they do not look too repulsive.[23]

The meat inspector inspects each bird in less than three seconds. He "must use sight, feel, and smell to examine all organs and tissues of the carcass, including the heart, liver, spleen, kidneys, lungs, air sacs, and skin. He is expected to protect the consumer from cancerous tumors, breast blisters, male sex organs, fecal contamination, feathers, lung tissue, and other unsanitary or diseased chicken parts."[24]

Now You See It—Now You Don't

Under the old meat inspection system, "an inspector condemned the whole chicken if he found a tumor or any part of it. The committee recommended that if a bird were found to have cancerous tumors on its wing or any other part, neither the part, much less the rest of the chicken, should go to waste; the cancerous part should be cut off and used in such products as hot dogs and the rest of the birds should be sold as cut up chicken.[25]

What About Poultry Plants?

We assume usually that meat plants take necessary precautions for sanitary conditions but: The General Accounting Office, in November, 1971, found more than half of the sixty-five poultry plants inspected were grossly contaminated. The local health inspector is the only person who tests bacteria counts in most chicken plants. He usually makes an annual visit to sample tap water that goes into the chiller; therefore, federally inspected poultry may be loaded with dangerous bacteria.

Poultry and Samonella Poisoning

Poultry is a very perishable food, and improper handling and cooking can readily cause samonella poisoning. However, samonella is caused by an organism which abounds in nature, but is easily killed by normal cooking heat. Always cook (any) meat, well done.

Consequenly most food poisoning occurs when food is inadequately cooked or is recontaminated by remaining

*for several hours in warm temperatures, or touched by
hands, cutting instruments, or cutting boards which
have previously come in contact with uncooked fowl or
other meat. The National Communicable Disease
Center estimates that two million Americans each year
are afflicted with the disease at an approximate cost of
$300 million....*

*Sudden causes of nausea, diarrhea, headache, and
fever are passed off as "twenty-four hour flu" when in
fact they have been caused by bacteria in unclean
appetizing food.*[26]

The more poultry is handled, the more contamination. If
the exposed skin is slick, be aware that the bacteria count is in
the millions.

The Plump Bird

Have you noticed the liquid draining off your defrosting
turkey? A weights-and-measures department exposed that
some 12 to 13 pound birds had up to one and a half pounds of
water frozen on them. That means we're paying meat prices for
frozen water. A bird ready for the freezer has usually been
presoaked in a water bath to "balloon" it, to make it appear
plump. The giblet bag inside the turkey may be a solid block of
ice.[27]

Where to Buy Poultry

You say it's impossible to raise your own chickens. I have a
friend who lives in a suburb with chickens in a shelter and a
small, clean run. But if this is too difficult, there are some conscientious farmers who raise healthy nutritious poultry. Do you
value your health? Check them out. Look for open-range
flocks, or well kept uncrowded, well-ventilated poultry houses.
And ask them what they're fed. (Feed mills will supply un-
medicated, untreated feeds upon request. See egg section.) If
all else fails, buy only inspected and graded fowl; it is safer than
ungraded. Also whole chickens appear to be a better health
buy than cut-up chickens.

Wholesome Meats—How Can You Tell?

You can't! Health officers explained that there is no way in
today's marketplace for a consumer to be sure that the fish,
meat, or chicken she is buying is wholesome. Sight and smell

are no longer to be trusted because the chemicals that are in use today can doctor decaying, diseased, or just plain stale food. All a consumer can do, they say, is to rely on the federal, state or local inspector and put his faith in the brand name and the store selling it.[28]

YOU THOUGHT IT WAS CHICKEN [29]

	How Much		How Much
Chicken ravioli	2%	Chicken pie	14%
Chicken soup	2%	Frozen Chicken Dinner	18%
Chop suey with chicken	2%	Creamed chicken	20%
Chicken chop suey	4%	Chicken carriatore	20%
Chicken chow mein with noodles	4%	Chicken fricassee	20%
Chicken chow mein without noodles	4%	Chicken a la King	20%
		Sliced chicken with gravy and dressing	25%
Chicken tamales	6%		
Noodles or dumplings with chicken	6%	Sliced chicken with gravy	35%
Chicken stew	12%	Minced Chicken Bar-B-Q	40%

"Note" A nutritionist informed me that this problem has since been upgraded. Check labels.

Preparing Live Chickens for the Freezer

You get better results in preparing live poultry meat if you starve your chickens for 22 to 24 hours but give them plenty of water. Bleed them well, then clean and dress. Don't bruise or tear flesh. Chill no more than two hours. (Wild duck or pheasant should be aged 2 or 3 days.) Clean out cavity and remove excess fat. Wrap giblets well, and store in cavity. Put in freezer bag and expel all air. Twist and fasten top. Old chickens keep well up to four months. Young chickens, ducks, and turkeys, nine months. Slight bone discoloration is normal during freezing. It's harmless. Don't freeze stuffing in poultry. It spoils too easily.

EXPENSIVE WATER

Approximate proportions:

Chicken Pot Pie——

Chili Con Carne——

Corn Beef Hash——

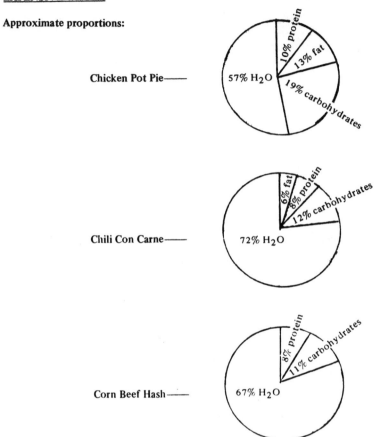

Section VI

Fishy News

As was mentioned, many of us ignore the dietary guidance given us in the Bible, but the "All Knowing Creator" knows concerning the foods he has created. In Leviticus chapter 11, verses 9-12, it advises us to eat only the meat in the waters with "fins and scales." All other living things that move in the waters are an abomination to us....I became quite indignant when I realized that "lobster tails with drawn butter" and those delicious "butterfly shrimp" have no fins or scales. However, being weak in the saliva buds, I have indulged. You decide concerning your indulgences. But evidence points to the wise biblical advice as being good practical advice. Here's why:

Some Fish Thrive on Filth

Just as the pig was created to help clean up the earth, the fish without "fins and scales" are known as the "garbage mouths" of the waters. They thrive on polluted waste and filth. Evidence confirms this....

The U.S. Army Biological Laboratory reports that California mussels are known to be poisonous to humans because they eat the organisms responsible for "red tide." And shellfish can become so toxic they have been responsible for human poisonings throughout the world.

The American Medical Association's *Archives of Environmental Health* pointed out that:

> The abililty of shellfish to act as vectors of human disease has been well documented. Early in this century the consumption of shellfish harvested from polluted water was shown to be the cause of typhoid fever outbreaks, and in the past ten years outbreaks of infectious hepatitis in this country and abroad have been associated with the consumption of oysters and clams.

*This epidemiological evidence has been supported
by a number of laboratory studies which have shown
that oysters and clams will not only take up a significant
amount of virus or bacteria from contaminated water,
but will concentrate these organisms to a level up to 60
times that of the surrounding water. Naturally occurring
contamination with certain types of echovirus and cox-
sackie virus has been demonstrated in oysters taken
from water frankly polluted with human wastes.*

*Paradoxically, shellfish grow best in areas most
likely to be contaminated with human waste.*

What Else is an Abomination?

In 1969, just over 2 percent of fish and fish products sold in
the United States had been inspected; in 1969, just over 1 percent of the fish processing plants and "fishing establishments
on shore" were inspected.

The reports from the U.S. Senate Hearings were: of the fish
plants that were checked, many were found to be deplorable.
Live and dead animals, rats, putrid odors, overflowing
cesspools, filthy meat smoking racks, dirty looking food
handlers, etc. were found.

Worst and Best Fish Mixed Together

Another unbelievable problem is that fish is highly
perishable, even moreso than meat and poultry. Fish requires
special handling because of rapid deterioration. Many plants
that care for fish products are small and don't have proper
facilities to prevent the fish from spoiling; therefore, much fish
can be low quality. They actually mix the bad fish with the
good—the consumer has no idea of the quality they're getting.

Senator Philip Hart of Michigan said "that once the fish is
on the shelf, the consumer doesn't know whether it is from the
finest of all plants or the worst of all." Up to 55 percent of fish
eaten in the United States is shipped from foreign countries.
Some have good inspection procedures and others don't in-
spect, period.

The Popular Fish—Canned Tuna

Since a billion and a half cans of tuna fish are consumed
annually in the U.S. be aware that this food is very rich in essential amino acids, vitamins, flourine and phosphorus.

However, a test disclosed "a disturbing number of rodent hairs, other animal hairs, fragments of feathers, moth scales, and insect and maggot parts," in samples tested. But the FDA allows this, so we just have to tolerate it, *because we have to eat.* The food research also points out that "In the kingdom of foods, canned tuna is thought to be a bargain source of protein."[30]

Are Fish Sticks a Good Buy?

Not so. According to a fish report, some packages of fish sticks tested had less than 60 percent fish—the rest breading, resulting in $1.42 a pound for the meat. Some samples were as high as 28 percent less weight than what was claimed on the package. A bacteriological test showed one particular brand to have an average plate count of 430,000 organisms per gram, an average of 32 coliforms per gram. These wouldn't present a health hazard if the sticks (large) were cooked for 15 minutes at 400 degrees.

Catch your own or buy fresh wholesome fish and dip them in thin batter or plain flour (see breads) for cooking.

Best Fish Buys

1. Knowing what you now know about fish, it's wise to catch your own in unpolluted waters (if you can find them).
2. Some stores advertise "fresh fish, from stream to store." These should be good buys.
3. A better level of quality is maintained for canned fish, than frozen, so canned fish is a better choice, than frozen.

What to Look for in Fresh Fish

Also try to buy fresh rather than frozen, because there is no way to tell if frozen fish is wholesome. Many stores, however, thaw frozen fish and label them as fresh.

Wholesome fish should:

1. Have clear, not clouded eyes.
2. Have a good color.
3. Have a fresh smell. A fishy smell isn't fresh.
4. Flesh that spring back when touched. Stale fish leaves indentations.
5. Smooth and firm skin.
6. Firm scales and a good sheen.

Smoked Meats and Other Foods

When we realize the possible health dangers of certain foods if eaten, it is evident why people are dying more often of cancer and heart disease. Here are some other suspected dangers:

Icelanders and others who eat large quantities of smoked fish have a high incidence of stomach cancer. The carcinogenic (cancer-causing) factors in the smoke is suspected of being a health hazard. For this reason it is prudent to avoid smoke-treated foods. This includes certain smoked fish, such an anchovies, sardines, salmon, eel; as well as other smoked foods, such as oysters, turkey, cheese, ham, bacon, etc. and charcoal broiled meat (outside barbequeing), burned toast, etc.'' We all eat some of these foods, some of the time, but do eat them in moderation.

When Buying Canned Meats

When buying canned meat, it appears that your canned ocean fish products have the least additives. Even though labels "don't tell all," some food, canned tuna, salmon, sardines, shrimp and even boned turkey have no listing at all of chemical additives. On the other hand, canned corned beef, potted and deviled meats, sandwich loaves, sandwich spreads, vienna sausage, etc. all have sodium nitrates, nitrites or both. (See harmful effects under sodium nitrites.)

Wild Meats

Due to so many unhealthy practices in the commercial meat department, the in-season wild meats would be a welcome addition to any table. Get your game licenses and head for the hills. (See "Eating What Comes Naturally" for cooking hints.)

Unhealthy Fowl

The "Dietary Judge" instructs us not to eat these fowl: the eagle; ossifrage (hawk family); ospray (American hawk); vulture; kite (a predatory bird from the hawk family); every raven after his kind; owl; cuckow; night hawk and the hawk after his kind; swan; pelican; gier eagle; stork; heron after her kind (wading birds with long necks, slender bills, and long legs); lapwing; and the bat.[32]

Consider These if You're Starving

The Bible, again, instructs us that we can eat every flying creeping thing that goeth on all four, which have legs above their feet, to leap withal upon the earth. Even these of them ye may eat; the locust after his kind, and the bald locust after his kind, and the beetle (yuk!) after his kind, and the grasshopper (ugh!) after his kind. But all other flying creeping things which has four feet, shall be an abomination to you.[34] (I include this information because if we are hungry, we might be grateful for any of the above.)[33]

The Findings of Protein Verses Carbohydrates

I know this information on meat is discouraging, but here are some encouraging facts. Dr. P.E. Allson of Brigham Young University in his compilation of experiments on athletes reports that "Accurate information concerning the type of fuel used by working muscles is essential for the intelligent planning of diets to meet the nutritional requirements of people...." The experiments indicate that most of our energy is derived from carbohydrates. When the carbohydrates are used up, the muscles derive energy from fat. In the same report, Dr. Donald L. Cooper, M.D., Director of Student Health Service and Team Physician for Oklahoma State University at the 43rd Annual Meeting of the American College Health Association explained that the heavy protein (meat-dominated) diet is the vogue trend, but "the athlete who eats steak, eggs, or other protein food before a contest is more apt to be troubled with acidosis, cramps, fatigue...carbohydrates are 10 percent more efficient than proteins or fats in utilizing oxygen." So those of you who want to build your muscles and avoid fatigue under stressful conditions (we're all under some stress) are advised to balance your diet but don't give proteins such a prestigious place in your diet. They are essential, but not in great amounts. Dr.

Cooper says that to think eating meat builds muscles, is like putting two and two together and getting five.[34]

How Much Meat to Purchase

Boneless—Ground meat, rolled roasts, cutlets, cubes, liver, boneless steaks—an average serving is ¼ pound per person. (Even though this meat is more expensive, oftentimes it's a better buy than meat with bones. Bones can be expensive.)

Medium bone—Roasts, steaks, chops, with moderate bone allow 1/3 to ½ pound per person.

Large bones—Short ribs, neck bones, oxtails, etc., allow 2/3 or more pounds per person.

Spice It Up

Early salting of meat during cooking draws out juices, so season later. Juices will remain in meat, however, if meat is seared before seasoning. Use about ¾ teaspoon seasoning per pound for ground meat; one or two teaspoons for two pounds of solid meat.

Other economical seasonings are to rub meat with garlic, onion, or other herbs, or sprinkle over surface a half hour or so before cooking.

To preserve top flavor of fatty meats, pour excess grease off after a half hour of cooking.

Cook It Correctly

There are two basic methods to cook meat: *dry heat* and *moist heat. Dry heat* methods are: broiling, panbroiling, pan-frying, oven roasting or baking. Dry heat methods are best for tender, fatty cuts. *Moist heat* methods are: stewing, simmering, braising and pot-roasting. Moist heat is used for less tender cuts of meat.

Method for Meat Cookery

	Beef	Veal	Lamb	Fish
Pan-Broiling:	Patties, small thin Steaks: Club, Cubed, Porterhouse, Rib, Round, Sirloin, T-bone	Patties	Patties	Fillets
Pan-Frying:	Liver, Patties with T.V.P.	Cube Steaks	Chops	Whole fish

	Beef	Veal	Lamb	Fish
Oven Roasting:	Chuck, Rib, Round, Rump, Shoulder, Sirloin, Tenderloin	Leg, Loin, Shoulder	Leg, Loin, Rib Shoulder	Whole fish
Pot-Roasting:	Flank, Liver, Round, Rump, Short Ribs, Shoulder, Sirloin Tip	Cutlets, Chops, Round, Shoulder and Rump Roasts	Breast, Neck, Shanks, Short Ribs, Shoulder Cuts	
Braising:	Chuck, Sweetbreads, Liver	Cutlets, Sweetbread	Breast, Sweetbreads	
Simmering:	Brisket	Breast	Breast	
Stewing:	Corned Beef, Heel of Round, Meat Bones, Neck, Shank, Short Ribs	Breast, Meat Bones, Riblets, Shanks	Breast, Meat Bones, Neck Slices, Shanks	

Let's Broil (See Meat Chart)

1. Meat broils better if at room temperature (70 degrees)—watch it, as bacteria growth is a problem.
2. Set oven on highest heat. Always preheat oven for roasting or broiling.
3. Trim or slash fat edges to prevent curling. Place meat 2 to 4 inches from heat depending on thickness.
4. Broil from 7 (medium) to 15 minutes (very well done) on each side, depending on desired doneness. Don't prick meat or you lose juiceness.

Let's Panbroil (See Meat Chart)

1. Place (lightly oiled—optional) meat in an open skillet. Don't add oil, water or lid.
2. Sear meat quickly until blood comes to top, then turn (usually one minute). Reduce heat and cook until done. Pour off excess fat or it will fry rather than broil. Meat that is turned often will dry out and toughen easily. Never turn steak more than once.
3. Season and serve.

Let's Panfry

1. Brown meat on both sides in an oiled skillet. Don't use lid.
2. Cook on low temperature until done.

Let's Oven-Roast (See Chart for meat to be Oven-roasted)

1. Preheat oven, and place meat, fat side up (fat bastes the meat) in a shallow pan or rack. If no fat side, put bacon or other fat on top for tender meat results. If using thermometer, insert into thickest part of meat, avoiding fat or bone.
2. Cook in moderate 325 degrees oven until thermometer registers done (usually 165 to 170 degrees F.) or use thermometer time table or cook 2 or 3 hours depending on size and desired doneness.
3. When done, take from oven, let stand 15 or so minutes to set juices before carving. Season before or after cooking. "NOTE" Oven roasting meat at 200 degrees for 12 hours doesn't insure safety in any meats, especially pork, because roasting is a reflected heat. Methods with moist heat, such as panroasting, stewing, crock pots, etc. is safe at lower temperatures because it's steam is more penetrating.

Let's Potroast (Braise)

1. Brown meat quickly. Place meat in large skillet.
2. Add boiling water (about 1 cup). Cover with tight lid. Simmer slowly on top of stove until done. Add more liquid if necessary.

Roasting Duck or Goose

These birds are extremely fat, so preroast for 15 minutes before stuffing. Because of fat taste, cooking the stuffing separately gives a better flavor. If not stuffing bird, put potatoes, peeled apples, onion, carrots in cavity, etc. to catch strong flavors. Discard vegetables before serving. These birds whether stuffed or not should be pricked generously and frequently for excess fat to escape. Preroast bird at 400 degrees for 15 minutes, then cook like a chicken, 20 minutes per pound at 325 degrees F. The bird will cook faster if hot spoons or forks are placed in the cavity.

Let's Stew

1. Cut meat in cube-size pieces.
2. Brown meat (see browning meat) first or drop raw cubes

into hot boiling water, trying not to disturb boil (for meat juice retention). When meat turns color, reduce heat to simmer.

3. Cover with tight fitting lid. Cook slowly until tender. Add more liquid if necessary. Don't boil meat. Rapid boiling ties up protein, and destroys food value.

Let's Fricasse

Stew meat (above) until tender. Remove meat and brown again in oil or butter. Thicken stew liquid, add browned meat. Serve as desired.

About Roasting in Foil

Roasting meat in foil entraps the steam, giving meat a stewed taste, so it's really not roasting, because roasting means ventilation. Caution—don't open foil to brown, it merely dries out meat.

Browning (Searing) Meat

For best results, wipe meat dry. Heat pan slowly and thoroughly, then add little oil only to cover bottom of pan. Add meat, turn frequently. Don't overcrowd pan or meat will be grey instead of brown. Add more oil if necessary rather than burn. Pour off excess fat before adding liquid for stewing. Or, when meat is half done, add vegetables quickly and stir often to prevent burning.

Marinated Meats

Marinating gives tenderness, but it also leaches away many valuable proteins and vitamins. Marinating 12 hours, cuts cooking time 1/3. Use ¼ cup marinade for every pound of food.

Tenderizing Marinades

1. Soak meat in buttermilk or sour milk (see about sour milk) 8 hours or longer. The lactic acid breaks down tough meat fibers. This method is also a preservative for meat if no refrigeration is available.

2. Soak in cider vinegar for two or more hours. (Evaporates in cooking.)

What About Commercial Meat Tenderizers?

Papain is a meat tenderizer injected directly into cattle and is also commonly used in homes and restaurants. Federal authorities haven't been too concerned over the use of papain because it is deactivated by cooking heat. However, papain could readily be present in rare meats and the possibility of internal damage has cause for concern.

The May 20, 1968, issue of the Journal of the American Medical Association reported death resulting from eating foods tenderized by papain.

Even if death doesn't result, papain is known to cause damage to the tissue in the mouth, throat and stomach, and when it is injected into rabbits it results in the progressive collapse of a rabbit's normally erect ears.[35]

Ruth Winter also noted that "earlier, experimental studies on fourteen dogs showed every animal receiving papain had some degree of damage to the esophageal wall, with reddening and thickening of the mucosal wall at the site of the lodged bolus. Advanced hemorrhagic pulmonary edema was found to be the cause of death in these animals."

These commercial meat tenderizers do more than break down the tissues in our meat: they can damage us in the process.

Pressure Cooker—The Emergency Pan

Pressure cook meats only in emergencies, as loss of food value is extremely high. Tests prove that these have more flavor and less shrinkage if cooked at 10 rather than 15 pounds pressure.

To Reheat Meat

It's advisable to slice meat for reheating as large pieces dry out before heat can penetrate. Put sliced meat in a steamer (see inexpensive vegetable steamer) to heat.

Variety Meats for Variety

Most variety meats are very nutritious and economical and do add spice to your menu. These include organ meats like sweetbreads, liver, kidney, brains; muscle meats such as heart, tongue, and tripe; bony meats like knuckle bones, tails, and marrow centers. It is important that these meats be fresh. Experiment with these in cooking, they can be delicious

Hints About Sweetbreads

Sweetbreads come from the pancreas, and the thymus gland of the animal. To prepare, first soak them in cold water one hour or more to release blood. Change water if necessary. Blanch them by boiling for 3 or 4 minutes, then place in cold water. Cool and remove tough membranes, etc. Cover with a weight and place in the refrigerator and leave whole or break carefully into pieces. One pair is needed for two servings. Now you may poach. stew. braise. broil or put in sauce.

Storing Raw Meat

REFRIGERATOR-Packaged meat in your refrigerator will last longer if commercial wrap is removed, then wrapped loosely so air can circulate through the meat. Store in coldest part of refrigerator. Steaks, chops, and roasts will keep up to three days in about 40 degree temperatures. Ground. chopped or cubed meat. use within 24 hours.
FREEZER-Freeze meat at 0 degrees F. or lower. Inexpensive butcher's paper is best for meat to protect against drying and freezer burn. Date your meat.

Salting-Brining-Drying-Smoking-Canning Meats

Call your extension service for these methods of preserving food.

Storing Cooked Meat

REFRIGERATOR-Cool cooked meat an hour before refrigerating, then wrap tightly to prevent drying. Sliced meat spoils more rapidly than roasts, etc. Store in coldest part of refrigerator. Will keep from 3 to 5 days.
FREEZER-Wrap well in butcher or moisture proof paper. Will keep three or four months with no loss of flavor.

Thawing Frozen Meat

Best to thaw in wrapper. If time permits. thaw in refrigerator—takes a day or two. Thawed meat should never be allowed to be warmed at room temperature (unless cooking methods advise) because of rapid bacteria growth. They say never refreeze thawed meat, but I've done it with success. Be careful, however.

How to Cook Frozen Meat

Frozen meats may be cooked, thawed or frozen: but thawed or partially thawed helps to retain juiciness even in stewing as the cold meat juices are released into the liquid. Meat to be breaded must be partially thawed. Cooking frozen roast or large cuts of meat takes 1½ required cooking time. When broiling frozen meat, place 5 or 6 inches from heat, again allow 1½ the cooking time.

Imitation Meat—
Textured Vegetable Protein

The soybean is an excellent source of vegetable protein. But T.V.P., as it has all come to be called, is abused as a natural food.

Many people are putting this refined food into storage. Moderation is the answer in using it:

Imitation meat products lack the vital vitamins and minerals present in meat. Real meat gives us valuable amounts of iron, thiamine, riboflavin, niacin, phosphorus; kidneys and liver give us vitamins A and B, iron phosphorus and the trace minerals. Textured vegetable soybean is usually 35 to 50 percent protein, 20 to 30 percent carbohydrates and up to 20 percent fat—no other nutrients are present unless synthetics are added.

Imitation meat is seasoned, held together, and colored with a flock of flavor enhancers, thickening agents, emulsifiers, artificial colorings and flavorings. A recipe for artificial bacon includes soy protein, hydolyzed yeast protein, salt, spices, monosodium glutamate, vegetable gum stabilizer, yeast, corn oil, artificial coloring, and water.[16]

Meat Substitute—Where Does it Come From?

Soybean is the source. The oil from the bean is removed, the protein that remains is dissolved, and the thickened substance is forced through thousands of tiny holes in a metal container, and the fibers are washed, colored, flavored and cooked.

Textured means it is given a structural quality of meat. This is done in three ways: spinning, extrusion or expansion.

Spinning Process-A solution high in protein is forced through a spinnerette into thousands of fine filaments. After it's spun it can be made to taste like most meats by adding fats, artificial flavorings, binders and colors.

Extrusion Process-Low concentrated vegetable protein is extruded like toothpaste from a tube under high pressure. It realigns the molecules, resulting in a meal-like texture (granules).

Expansion Process-The mixture is quickly released to return to atmospheric pressure.

Imitation meat, i.e., the hamlike breakfast slices, etc., having a bologne-like texture, is highly refined and is quite expensive. The meat extenders (granules, etc.) require less refining, and are considerably less expensive.

How Nutritious—Really?

As was previously mentioned, T.V.P. consists of protein, fat and carbohydrates. The Food and Drug Administration is establishing nutritional standards for this new food and they should be out soon, as these food substitutes vary drastically in quality. Some varieties are boosted with synthetic vitamins and minerals, and some are not boosted period.

Brain Damage Additive

Some of these products have many additives: such as, monosodium glutamate (MSG), titanium dioxide, dicalcium phosphate, ferrous sulfate, disodium inosinate, and disodium guanylate, etc.

Monosodium glutamate (MSG) causes brain damage in young rodents and brain damage effects in rats, rabbits, chicks and monkeys. High concentrates of titanium dioxide dust may cause lung damage. Ferrous sulfate is used to treat iron deficiency anemia, but it's also used as a wood preservative, weed killer; and large quantities can cause gastrointestinal disturbances.[37] All T.V.P. doesn't have preservatives so for top health and dollar, buy those without additives, if possible.

Artificial Meat has Cause for Concern

Consumer Research Magazine, October, 1973, reports new items such as refined soybean products and single cell protein derivatives have already caused concern. These foods, according to *The Lancet,* must be watched for contamination, high nucleic-acid content, and causation of allergies, which have already started to appear. *The Lancet* suggests new foods should be as carefully monitored as new drugs. "If they are introduced widely and contribute to the cause of diseases that appear after a long latent period, we may be in great trouble."[38]

T.V.P. reminds me personally of cold cereal. Not in taste and texture but in the way it's processed. It is a highly refined product and should never replace food. Just use it in moderation or use it as a food extender (like bread crumbs in a meat loaf).

A Positive Note

Dr. Aaron Altschul of Georgetown University Medical School, Washington, D.C., an internationally respected nutritionist, sees textures protein as a "very exciting development—I have compared it (in importance) with the invention of bread." He says, "It's almost analogous."

He belittles esthetic protests against "manufactured foods."

Bread and pasta, he points out, are manufactured foods. Unless wheat were made into one or the other, it would stand in the field pretty much inedible.[39]

Other Ways of Cutting Meat Costs

Why not use the *natural soybean* as a meat extender? Soak them 24 hours (rinse several times during soaking); grind or use whole in meat loaves, casseroles, soups, etc. Even though the soybean is weak in a couple of amino acids, it's an unrefined valuable food. It's a far superior nutritional buy than imitation meat products.

If You're Using Extenders, Here's What to Do!

When adding extenders to meat loaf, etc., use approximately 2/3 meat and 1/3 extender, or follow package directions. The directions allow for top meat flavor, juiciness and shape. When too much extender is added, you get off-flavor and loaves and patties will fall apart.

Extenders added to ground meat, etc., gives less shrinkage, because the extender absorbs and holds meat juices. The unflavored T.V.P. product can be added to anything as it picks up the flavor. Top quality T.V.P. can be added by itself to chili, casseroles, etc.

High quality T.V.P. granules make (occasional) quick sandwiches. Pour warm water over granules. Let sit ten minutes. Add salad dressing for a quick spread.

Storing T.V.P.

For use and storage, look for "Fortified or Enriched" and no preservatives, if possible.

Dry mix T.V.P. should be stored in a dry cool place. It is a grain product that will spoil quickly unless special care is taken. Packed in bags, it should be used within six months to one year. When vacuum sealed in inert nitrogen, a can of T.V.P. should keep for several years.

When T.V.P. is reconstituted, it should be treated like fresh meat, i.e., kept refrigerated and used withing about three or four days.

It can be frozen in any form, dry, cooked loaves, patties etc., or in casseroles, etc.

Part 5

Produce

Problems

Commercial Produce—
How Good, How Safe?

You cannot be fully aware of the cardboard leathery flavor of commercial vegetables and fruits until you've eaten home grown foods or bought them from the roadside fruit and vegetable stands. Commercial fruits and vegetable buyers stress uniformity of size and color, so the appearance will entice the customer. There seems to be little thought to nutrition, flavor and safety, especially with the unbelievable amount of pesticides, chemicals and additives allowed in foods.

The FDA Papers in their report "Pesticides, A Report On Residues In Food," June 1967, shows a full-page colored picture of a family sitting around a picnic table eating hot dogs, potato chips, tomatoes, chocolate cake, milk, etc. with these words, "American consumers of all ages may be confident that their foods are free from harmful amounts of pesticide residues, due to FDA's tolerance setting and enforcement procedures. Analyzes of raw agricultural products as well as total diet surveys show that pesticide residues are much lower than the amounts judged to be safe by FDA and the World Health Organization."

The picture and information are misleading, as pesticides in our foods are higher than we realize, as *Wall Street Journal* pointed out in Nov. 28, 1969, "There's more pesticides in our foods than Uncle Sam's random sampling methods might disclose."

Can You Rinse, Scrub or Peel
Chemicals Off Food?

The answer is No! Dr. O.W. Grussendorf, researcher, Canada Dept. of Agriculture points out that, "the residues are mainly in the entire system of the plant....We must distinguish somewhat between 'deposits' on the surface and 'residues' in the sense of contamination; both are 'residues' in the sense of contamination, and are objectionable per se. The chemicals are intimately interwoven in the structure of the plant. The insecticide can be entirely intra-cellular, and nothing of it can be found on the surface of the plant."[2]

It is estimated that 42 growth regulating chemicals are now approved by the USDA for more than 100 different uses in producing crops. One single test can determine up to 54 pesticide chemicals which are used to control pests.[3]

Until the biological effects of a compound known to have some toxic properties have been established through adequate research, that compound must be assumed, potentially dangerous.[4]

Many Additives are Never Checked

Would you believe that many additives are never checked that go into foods. The FDA admits that it is almost impossible to check procedures of small manufacturing plants around the country. Do you have any idea how much of our food comes from small manufacturing plants? Also the foods that are shipped from state to state are checked periodically, but foods that are shipped within a state are almost never checked. Any additives or procedures could be used.

"Gras List"
Is No Real Guarantee of Safety

The FDA has a list of additives listed as GRAS (generally recognized as safe). Some of these additives have been tested, but some of these tests are very inadequate. One example, the FDA sent out questionaires to 900 scientists regarding safety of certain additives. Only about 1/3 of the scientists responded and only 1/3 of those put any comments that were felt at all beneficial. From this minimal response they dropped three additives from the original published GRAS list. Many additives on the list have never been checked because there seems to be no ill effects on the people. (While we suffer from migraines, upset stomachs, unexplained birth defects and crib deaths etc.) It sometimes takes cancer 20 years to take it's deadly toll. What happens in a few years when they realize what problems some of these chemicals have imposed upon the health of the American public? Nothing. There is nothing we can do, but suffer the devastating consequences.

Our Preserved, Gassed, Dyed, Waxed, Chemically "Fresh Food"

Some stores take pride in selling local produce. Locally grown food is usually far superior to commercial produce shipped long distances. Fresh foods shipped cross-country and even from out-of-state may be shot with preservatives, sprayed with pesticides, washed in chemical baths, gassed, dyed and waxed. Let's look at the tomato....

Red Tomatoes? Certainly! Gassed Tomatoes? Certainly!

Machine harvesting of tomatoes has its problems, as the machine can't tell green tomatoes from red ones. So it automatically picks both. The USDA permits gassing of green tomatoes with ethylene to "hurry-up" the ripening process.[5]

Tomatoes Four Years Old? You Betcha!

A lot of commercial products are ripened with artificial methods. The food can be gassed or treated with artificial harmones, or you name it. If you've ever tasted home grown tomatoes or any home grown produce for that matter, you don't have to be an expert to tell the difference.

One method tested for tomatoes is to soak them in a sulphur dioxide bath. This procedure will actually keep tomatoes looking *fresh* for *three* to *four* years. Just for the record, sulphur dioxide is listed as GRAS (generally recognized as safe) on the FDA list of additives. It's a known air pollutant, and if concentrated amounts are inhaled it can cause death. In other words they tell us we can eat it but don't inhale it. Confusing isn't it?

You Thought It was Tomato Juice?

If you want to read about what's replacing natural foods, get some copies of *Food Technology* and read their ads. Here's how one ad reads: "Tomato Juice without tomatoes? There's no limit to the possible uses of specialty synthetic flavors in substitute and natural foods. Kohnstamm's sophisticated second generation of flavors doesn't stop at a convincing forgery of vine-ripened tomato. It includes...hordes of other fool-the-tongue tastes." Read labels carefully to avoid this deception.

Most Produce is Picked Green

Most produce grown for commercial purposes is picked green. This procedure alone, robs us of many valuable vitamins and minerals. Then fall and winter vegetables are usually grown in greenhouses with very little sun. Tomato plants grown in this manner produced fruit with one half as much ascorbic acid as that contained in plants grown outside in summer. However, let's emphasize that there would be little year 'round produce without winter greenhouses, even if it's inferior in quality. Learn to grow your own produce. You can store most of it all winter.

Nobody Persecutes These Drug Pushers

The *"mad manufacturers" think of everything. Regardless of what problem a food has, they can think of a way to fix it.* Isn't it funny how they persecute *drug pushers* in this country, but nobody says much to the *food drug pushers.* Just a thought...if drugs are forced on us indirectly (through food) nobody says a word.

Anyway, melons have their own inner natural gas that is naturally released to ripen mature fruit. If these foods are picked green the gas is never released to do the job, and the normal ripening process never takes place. But to make them appear ripe they may also give bananas, pears, melons, cantaloupe, oranges, lemons, tomatoes etc., good stiff shots of ethylene gas. The gas gives the outside a healthy appearance. What takes place after that can be a number of things such as being sprayed with artificial dyes, waxed or dipped in mineral oil, then wrapped in treated paper to prevent mold...We poor homemakers buy this food hoping to keep our families healthy.

Old Food? You'll Never Recognize It!

Do you think the food industries are clever because they can ripen green foods with a quick shot of gas? Well that's nothing. They can actually treat *old* food with antioxidants and make them appear *fresh.* Antioxidants can also delay the browning of such foods as potatoes, apples, apricots, pears, cherries and bananas.

Other Produce Problems

Potatoes aren't only treated with antioxidants. Experiments confirm that potatoes exposed to radiation won't sprout (foods that won't sprout are dead.) Potatoes are also subject to other sprout inhibitors and many are cited as being hazardous. Maleic hydrozide, a common antisprouting agent in potatoes, onions and other foods is a highly toxic substance causing liver damage in mice, problems with the nervous system in humans (how are your nerves?) and is suspected of playing *tic, tac, toe* with our genes and chromosomes.

Stale white potatoes may be dyed red to make them look like *fresh red potatoes.* Sweet potatoes and yams that might look a bit pale are usually dyed bright orange, just because. Topless carrots may be subjected to chemicals to inhibit enzyme growth, so more tops won't sprout. Possibly carrots with tops are better buys. I'm not sure at this point. Many fruits and vegetables are coated with waxes that are warned of being carcinogenic, including strawberries, oranges, lemons, limes, pears, apples, plums, peaches, melons, nectarines, carrots, cucumbers, parsnips, pumpkins, squash, tomatoes, peppers, egg plant, avocados, potatoes, and any other food that might look more appealing if it's shiny. Some of these waxes might not be a problem if the food is peeled, but peelings are very nutritious, and a lot of precious nutrition in food is just under the skin. If we peel too much we lose too much nutrition; if we don't peel enough we could be eating carcinogenic waxes. By the way have you ever tried peeling a strawberry? Just for the record, cabbages and similar foods are so loaded with chemicals it's impossible to even begin to clean them up. Most pesticide contamination is in the entire system of the plant.

The Chemical Orange

Have you noticed the mouth-watering shiny pieces of fruit on commercial display? Let me tell you why they look so enticing.

These fruits (also chocolates) are usually coated with carnauba wax (used in polishes, varnishes and deodorants); shellac; silicone; or mineral oil (see mineral oil). And if your children eat an unpeeled orange that is cut in half or quartered, they could be consuming the above coatings.

Oranges are almost always picked green, so the orange growers can *quickly* get their almighty money. Green oranges won't ripen once they've been picked, they merely spoil. So they are gassed until they turn a sickly white color. The oranges (whities) are then heated, washed and dipped in a hot vat or sprayed with a hot red No. 2 dye (a questionable dye). Citrus fruits may be wrapped in a diphenyl wrapping material to prevent mold growth and to prevent you from telling the age of the fruit. They are then shipped to the stores and we buy and eat them as a healthful snack.

Do you know what's so disheartening about the above information? Oranges are a very durable fruit. They could be allowed to ripen naturally on the trees (they will actually hang for weeks after ripening, without spoiling). The fruit could be shipped in refrigerated cars to all parts of the country as a wonderful natural food.

Citrus Peel, Normally a Very Nutritious Food

Are you aware that orange peel, cup for cup, is more nutritious than the orange? It is hailed as a cure for some illnesses and the former Dr. Clive McKay reports that it will control diarrhea in infants. The white of the orange is supposed to help prevent disease.

You could dry citrus peelings on a plate on your kitchen cupboard, put them in your blender and make wonderful fruit powders, You could add the fruit powder peel to gelatins, ice cream, candy and other recipes, but oh no! we dare not eat the citrus peel because it is so polluted with pesticides, gasses and unhealthy dyes.

If You Want a Good Orange?

A few outlets guarantee or list *vine, tree or naturally ripened* fruit. Or you can send directly to some companies and get untreated fruit. Also take note that the greenish, brownish or bruised-looking oranges are better choices than the bright orange ones (they are both the same on the inside). Also, heavy citrus fruits (weigh them in your hand) are better buys than light weight; they have more juice. We should demand that the manufacturers inform us whether or not fruit has been treated....Did you know that Canada and Great Britain won't allow much of our commercial food, including the *dyed orange* into their countries because of possible health hazards.

Man-made Food—the Buck Maker

Our mighty creator created all foods necessary for infinite health. Every living organ and bodily function can be superbly maintained by His magnificent natural resources. Then man came along with his refined sugar, refined flour and artificial products. At this point our inner ecology started to falter. Our creator didn't intend that our bodies be filled with foreign materials. Man-made foods are foreign materials, and offer little nutrition. Some of these products confuse the body. (See margarine.)

Some of the best comparisons of artificial products being unwisely consumed are margarine instead of butter; artificial eggs, artificial milk, artificial dairy whips, etc. Let's also take a look at what's replacing citrus fruits, namely, the orange.

The orange is a famous contributor of vitamin C. But what is never mentioned is that the orange also has varying amounts of calcium, phosphorus, iron, sodium potassium, vitamin A, thiamine, riboflavin, niacin, ash, carbohydrates, fat, protein, and possibly a hundred other benefits not yet discovered.

In many families the orange is being replaced with a popular powdered drink. These artificial drinks (and other fake foods) are a very poor buy for your health and food dollar. They are filled with refined sugar, artificial additives, and synthetic vitamins. How can these products replace life-giving foods? They can't in any sense. These artificial products aren't food. They are not made to improve your health; they are made to make money for the manufacturers. Nothing more. Go back to the wonderful God given natural foods that feed you. Improved health will be your reward. A dyed orange is far superior to sweetened, colored water.

What About Fruit Juices and Fruit Drinks?

Benzoic acid (mildly irritates the eyes, skin and mucous membranes) and sodium benzoic (2 grams will kill a dog) are commonly used in fruit juices, confectionery, jams, jellies, margarine, pickles, etc. Clarifying agents are added to some citrus flavored drinks to make them look clear, then clouding agents are added to make them look less clear. They think of everything don't they?

We, the consumer have to take some of the blame for the deplorable food situation because we won't buy certain products unless they look *a certain way*. The manufacturers adjust foods for *customer appeal*, even if the adjustments are detrimental to health. Most arguments of nutritionists are that commercial foods regardless of added problems *have some* nutrition, and nutrition even though it isn't the most desirable, DOES prevent starvation. I AGREE WHOLEHEARTEDLY. My goal is to teach you enough about commercial foods that when you have a choice you can make the best choice for your health and food dollar. So let me inform you concerning beverages....

Buy "Juices" Not "Drinks"

Avoid buying beverages that are labeled "drinks," as these beverages are mostly water, sugar and additives. Look for the labels that say "juice," because juices are made out of fruit. Commercial fruits have problems, granted, but they are far superior to sugared water with chemicals....Some drinks also say "10 percent fruit juice." These are also poor purchases as real juice is 100 percent juice, not 90 percent sugar, water, and artificial colorings etc.

Juices that say *unsweetened* or *no sugar* are your best juice buys.

About Commercial Frozen Vegetables and Fruits

A home freezer is a wise investment as home frozen foods, if frozen and cared for properly, are excellent foods with high nutritional values.

Freezing preserves foods naturally. No additives are necessary. Ethylenediaminetetracetic acid (used in pharmacies) may be added to commercial frozen fruits etc. This acid is used to eliminate foreign chemical tastes in foods. Many frozen foods are chemically preserved, chemically colored and have artificial flavors, not to mention the same farmer who loads the produce with excessive pesticides and nitrates also supplies the food for the frozen food companies.

Detergent residues have been found in frozen fruits and vegetables when examined, from the initial washings of the food. Microwave methods of blanching certain foods results in high losses of nutrients.[6]

If frozen foods are thawed or partially thawed and refrozen, the food loses nutrients and flavor. Some samples of frozen foods when examined had dangerous bacteria counts because of improper refrigeration. However if I had to choose, I'd personally take commercial frozen fruits and vegetables over commercially canned products. You decide.

Section II

Freeze Your Own

Freezing is an excellent way to preserve food, because bacteria can't grow in zero temperatures. ALWAYS FREEZE FOODS QUICKLY by placing them against the sides of your freezer or freezing units. Space packages to be frozen apart if possible. Stack frozen foods after they are frozen, not before. Foods consist of microscopic cells containing moisture. When foods are slowly frozen the icy pockets expand too slowly and rupture cells. These foods when thawed lose large amounts of juice, flavor and nutrients.

When foods are *quick frozen,* the cells remain firm and intact. If convenient, take large amounts of foods to be frozen to a locker for quick freezing.

About Freezing Vegetables

Most vegetables to be frozen should be steamed in a wire basket about two inches above boiling water for three or four minutes. (see vegetable steamer) Immediately put in very cold water, drain, then package in moisture proof bags or containers. Do most vegetables using the above method, except steam broccoli for 5 minutes. Many farmers freeze their corn without blanching. Some cut it off; others freeze it right on the cob, while others freeze it, husk and all. This will work, but there is some loss of nutrients. When thawing corn on the cob, defrost in refrigerator, eliminates the cob taste.

Vegetable Cubes Are Handy

Raw vegetables juice or puree will freeze well without precooking, such as tomato puree. You can add garlic and oregano etc., (excellent for spaghetti, casseroles etc). Put any clean, quartered vegetables in blender, make puree or juice, then freeze. Add green peppers, onion, any vegetables to tomato juice and season, for V8 type juice. If you freeze puree or juice in ice cubes, they are simple to use. Just put in plastic bags and use cubes as needed. (Much cheaper than canned, and more nutritious.) Make all kinds of vegetable juice cubes to add to stews, soups, etc.

How to Freeze an Orchard

Fruits to be frozen need no precooking. Fruits freeze well, but thaw softer than fresh. To prepare, wash gently. Never let foods stand in water, as water soluble vitamins leach away rapidly and fruits will become water soaked and mushy. Some fruits need no sweetner etc. to be frozen, but some fruits have better texture and flavor if preserved in a honey or sugar syrup.

About Honey and Sugar for Preserving

I don't like to add sugar to fruit, it's merely putting refined sugar on natural sugar. However, a 40 percent syrup is recommended for most fruits (3 cups sugar to 4 cups water). If using sugar, I just use from 1/3 to ½ the amount of sugar called for. You decide. To add sugar syrups to fruit, bring your syrup to a boil, cool then add it to fruit. Syrup should cover fruit. I also use honey to preserve fruits and it's delicious. When using honey for preserving you can cut the sweetner in half. For example if it says to use ½ to 1 cup of sugar per pint, use ¼ to ½ cup honey per pint.

Honey syrup for preserving fruit: A *thin syrup* is, 1 cup honey to 3 cups hot water. Cool all syrups before using. A *medium syrup* is, 2 cups honey to 2 cups hot water. Completely cover fruit with syrup. It usually takes ½ cup honey syrup for each pint. One cup for a quart. Mild, light honey is best for freezing fruit.

To sweeten fruits without syrups—merely drizzle honey or sprinkle sugar in desired amounts and mix through gently.

Unsweetened—Pack fruit into containers without adding liquid or sweetner, or cover with lemon juice and water, or ascorbic acid, or use fruit's own juice.

Some fruits darken during freezing and preparation, so it's recommended to add ascorbic acid in your syrups, sugars or juices. (Crushed vitamin C pills—more expensive—may be used, crystalline form, ascorbic acid, lemon juice etc.) Follow directions on package or just use a little bit mixed in your fruit, not much is needed.

Pack fruit in bowls, glasses, bags, jars etc., use ½ to 1 inch head room for expansion. Make sure you have good lids or tops.

Fruit Lovers Frozen Hints

Freeze only mature fruit.
Browning of fruit appears when almost all of the ascorbic acid has been oxidized.
Pick berries in the evening when berries are cool. Berries need no sweetener. Wild blue berries, a one minute scalding will prevent the skins from toughening. Bush berries pack whole or pitted.
Drizzle honey right over sliced or whole strawberries, ¼ cup to a pint and toss gently.
Fruits such as peaches and apricots etc. should be peeled before freezing. Dip in boiling water for easy removal of skins. Pears should be peeled by hand.
Pears, peaches, apricots, sweet cherries, figs etc. darken easily during freezing. To help retain color put in a syrup with a little added lemon juice.
Pack fruits gently but tightly. Fill pint container to ½ inch from top, qt. ¾ inch from top. Add enough syrup so fruit is covered. Crumble piece of parchment paper or cellophane to keep fruit emerged.
Apricot skins tend to toughen during freezing.
Wash and stem grapes, then pack seedless types whole. Cut others in half, remove seeds and freeze dry or in thin syrup.
Stem and pit sour cherries after chilling in ice water to minimize loss of juice. Add small amount of honey and pack.
Apples: Peel and slice. Pack dry or add 2 to 4 tablespoons honey with 2 tablespoons lemon juice to retain color.
Cantaloupe: Cut fresh in slices, cubes or balls. Add sweetener if desired. Serve slightly frozen for best texture.
Figs: Leave whole, slice or crush. Cover with thin syrup.
Dates: Leave whole or puree.
Plums if freestone, freeze readily just washed and pitted, either in halves or quarters. If clingstone, make puree.
Rhubarb freezes best from early crop. Wash and cut into 1 inch pieces. Pack dry or in a thin syrup. However, rhubarb will keep merely in jars of water with lids. No preserving is necessary.

APPROXIMATE YIELD OF FROZEN FRUITS FROM FRESH

Fruit	Fresh, as Purchased or Picked	Frozen
Apples	1 bushel (48 pounds)	32 to 40 pints
	1¼ to 1½ pounds	1 pint
Apricots	1 bushel (48 pounds)	60 to 72 pints
	2/3 to 4/5 pound	1 pint
Berries	1 crate (24 quarts)	32 to 36 pints
	1 1/2 to 1½ pints	1 pint
Cantaloupes	1 dozen (28 pounds)	22 pints
	1 to 1¼ pounds	1 pint
Cherries, sweet or sour	1 bushel (56 pounds)	36 to 44 pints
	1¼ to 1½ pounds	1 pint
Currants	2 quarts (3 pounds)	4 pints
	¾ pound	1 pint
Peaches	1 bushel (48 pounds)	32 to 48 pints
	1 lug box (20 pounds)	13 to 20 pints
	1 to 1½ pounds	1 pint
Pears	1 bushel (50 pounds)	40 to 50 pints
	1 to 1¼ pounds	1 pint
Plums and prunes	1 bushel (56 pounds)	38 to 56 pints
	1 to 1½ pounds	1 pint
Raspberries	1 crate (24 pounds)	24 pints
	1 pint	1 pint
Rhubarb	15 pounds	15 to 22 pints
	2/3 to 1 pound	1 pint
Strawberries	1 crate (24 quarts)	38 pints
	2/3 quart	1 pint

Includes blackberries, blueberries, boysenberries, dewberries, elderberries, gooseberries, huckleberries, loganberries, and youngberries.

(Chart: U.S. Department of Agriculture)

Fruit Cubes Have Many Uses

Wash, pit or core fruit (don't peel), quarter and put in blender, colander etc. Only add tiny amounts of water, if necessary, to make puree. Pour puree in ice cube trays to make fruit cubes. Put frozen cubes in plastic bags and keep in your freezer. Fruit ice cubes are delicious if warmed slowly and served over cake or ice cream. The frozen cubes are soft enough, to insert a toothpick in, for popsicles. Also they make yummy milkshakes, just pour milk over cubes in blender. Try them as warm syrup for pancakes or on toast or use them to flavor a batch of homemade ice cream. There's no limit to the use of frozen fruit cubes. The fruit puree can also be frozen in ketchup or oil bottles, or any bottle or jar you'd normally throw out. Leave two inches at top for expansion. Thaw and use over ice cream, waffles, for fruit drinks etc.

If Electricity Goes Off

(Note) If your power ever goes off, and you have a freezer full of food, don't open your freezer door if possible. A full freezer will stay frozen for two days even in summer if not opened unnecessarily. If power isn't resumed after one or two days, dry ice (25 lbs. in a 10 cubic foot cabinet) will hold the temperatures below freezing in a less than half full freezer for two or three days—a full freezer, three to four days.

Those Commercially Canned Vegetables, Fruits and Misc. Foods

Americans eat a lot of canned foods as they are readily available and can be stored easily, but the practices of the commercial canners are questionable as far as health is concerned.

Home canners dip their fruits and vegetables in hot water to remove skins quickly; commercial canners may use chemical or lye baths for easy removal of skins.

Have you ever wondered why your home canned foods aren't as firm as those in the store? It's because those nice firm commercially canned tomatoes, peas, pickles, etc., have additives such as magnesium chloride, alums (concentrated amounts cause intestinal bleeding, kidney damage, gum problems and have caused death in humans), or calcium citrate added to maintain firmness.

Magnesium carbonate is used in green peas and tin dichloride is used in asparagus to keep them green. Sulphur dioxide is added to almost all corn products. Ferrous gluconate (may cause gastrointestinal problems) is added to olives to give them a nice uniform black color. Erythrosine (Red no. 3) is used in fruit cocktail and cherry pie fillings and mixes.

They Are Worried About the Can What About Our Stomachs?

In the January 22, 1966, *Health Bulletin,* "Foods Gaining Ability to Eat Through Cans," it pointed out that excess amounts of nitrates in canned tomatoes and sweet potatoes could easily be the culprit of internal can corrosion.

Sugar and salt are added to canned foods (see sugar). Too much salt is suspected of contributing to the tendency to increase blood pressure and to interfere with absorption of food if taken in large amounts over a period of time.[7] Americans consume 20 times more salt than they need.

Here are some percentages of sodium increases in canned vegetables:

45,554 percent in green beans
5,857 percent in asparagus
450 percent in tomatoes
367 percent in carrots

This information only touches the commercial canned food problem. See bibliography.

Should Foods Be Stored in an Open Can?

The answer is *No,* The National Canners Association and the USDA in their 1965 yearbook says that consumers can store canned foods in open cans without problems but tests suggest otherwise. "After a can has been opened, tin contamination of the food remaining in it may rise by leaps and bounds. For example, when canned grapefruit was first opened and tested, the juice contained 20.3 milligrams per kilogram of tin; after two days, 87; and after four days, 364."[9]

These Canned Foods Shouldn't Be Eaten

Canned goods aren't edible if you sense any of the following: bulging tops, sides or bottoms of cans; seepage anywhere; dents along seam lines of cans; off odors: off colors; foaming or a milky liquid. If any of these above signs are prevalent, open can, don't taste, and put in disposal to protect humans and animals.

How Could Canned Foods Be Improved?

Home canners don't put chemical additives in their canned foods, so why should commercial manufacturers? Chemicals, artificial food colors and other additives are added for consumer appeal.

Also, commercial canned foods may sit in hot warehouses for years before they ever hit the grocers shelves, and it's a known fact that canned foods lose nutrients when stored for any length of time, especially in warm storage areas. Dates should be printed on every can so a consumer can understand them. Most dated products are printed with a code so only the manufacturers can understand them. I'd personally like to know if canned foods were canned this year or three years ago. Wouldn't you?

Home Canning—Fun and Economical

Canning food at home is fun and economical and the home canned product, if canned properly, supplies more healthful foods than commercially canned products. Consult your extension agent. They have free canning instructions for the asking. Follow their instruction precisely. (See about *Cooking Home Canned Vegetables,* in this book.)

Yield of Preserving Fruits and Vegetables

Vegetable	lbs. per quart	Qts. per Bushel	Fruit	lbs. per quart	Qts. per Bushel
Lima Beans in Pod	2	7	Apples	2½	28
Beans, snap	1¾	17	Berries	1 1/3	24
Beets	2¾	18	Cherries	1 1/3	20
Carrots	2¾	18	Peaches	2¼	21
Corn (off cob)	7 ears	8	Pears	2¼	30
Greens	2	7	Plums	2	28
Okra	2	17			
Peas in Pod	2	6			
Squash, Summer	2	18			
Sweet Potatoes	2½	20			
Tomatoes	3	18			

Again, your local extension services have every method of preserving food free for the asking. Call them.

Check Those Expiration Dates
(If You Can Understand Them)

Check expiration dates of all foods purchased. Don't buy foods on or after expired dates for top food value. The dates of frozen foods are indented on the carton or wrapper, usually at the end of the container. Cans have code number usually stamped on the bottom of the can. Boxes have indented codes or dates usually on the end of the box. Most states require dating of dairy products so you can easily tell when the products have expired.

What About Commercial Dehydrated Foods?

Drying your own or buying the popular bulk dehydrated foods is an excellent way to keep a year's food supply (everyone should have a year's supply of food on hand for emergencies). However, some companies are using many unhealthy additives in these foods. Sulphur dioxide is a deadly ingredient added to dried foods; fresh fruits; sliced fruits in restaurants; corn products such as frozen or canned corn, corn oil, corn starch, etc.; fruit juices; grains and the list could go on and on. There is also no limit to the amount of sulphur dioxide that can be used as an additive. The only restriction is that it can't be used in foods known to be a good source of Vitamin B-1.[10]

Scientific experiments on humans reported that from three tenths sulphur dioxide (amounts found on six to eight ounces of dried fruit) up to one gram daily developed signs of injury in humans, including nausea, anemia, dull eyes, destruction of blood corpuscles, inflammed mucous membranes, listlessness, etc.[11] So avoid foods with this additive, if possible.

On one #10 can of dehydrated applesauce the label lists: Dehydrated apples, (processed with sulphur dioxide, calcium sterate added) sugar, lemon powder (lemon juice combined and powdered with added dextrin, maltose and dextrose. BHT added as an antioxidant to the oil.)

BHT (butylated hydroxytoluene) is listed as GRAS (generally recognized as safe) on the FDA list of food additives. Yet Loyola University scientists reported on April 14, 1972, that pregnant mice fed a diet consisting of one half of one percent of BHT (or BHA) gave birth to offspring that frequently had chemical changes in the brain and subsequent abnormal behavior patterns.[12]

Dehydrated foods are such marvelous storage foods, they should be available as unadulterated food sources. Refuse to buy those with harmful additives, and let's bet the manufacturers do something about it. Buy those without additives; they are available.

Dry Your Own Food—

An Ancient, Effective Way to Prevent Starvation

The Indians kept from starving by drying most of their foods in the sun. Because of canning supply shortages, drying foods is again becoming a popular method of preserving edible commodities.

Nutrition and calories are highly concentrated in these foods, when you realize it takes 11 pounds of fresh apricots to yield 2 pounds of dried ones. Most dried fruits also dry to 75 percent natural sugar. It takes one-fourth the space to store dried products, verses canned; dried foods are light weight and easy to transport if you move; they are handy nutritious snacks; and are unexcelled as convenience foods in cooking. Dehydrated onions are a popular example of dried produce.

How to Dry Food

Moisture and warmth encourage enzyme action in foods, and creates spoilage. When these factors are removed, the enzymatic action is suspended and spoilage is retarded. To remove moisture from food you need warm moving air. You can achieve this with three effective methods: 1. The sun if available. 2. A commercial or homemade dehydrator. 3. The oven.

Let's Dry Fruits

You prepare food the same regardless of what drying method you use. Pit or core fruits (peeling cuts drying time in half) and cut them in halves, quarters, slices or shreds. Put foods on screens, or anything that will allow air to circulate on top and bottom and place in the sun. A good commercial dehydrator is worth the investment, or instructions for a homemade dehydrator are available.* For oven drying, prop oven door open ½ inch for electric, eight inches for gas. Keep heat lowest temperature (150 degrees on top shelf). Fruit on the outside will dry sooner, remove when dry. When fruit is pliable and leathery it's dry. A piece of screen cut the size of your oven trays works well. Cool and package at once. Pack in containers with tight lids etc. Store in a dark, dry, cool place.

Dry Fruit With Fun—Make Fruit Leather

One summer my family and I made over 100 yards of fruit leather. It's a fun versatile food, as you can send it through the mail, put in in lunches, take it on picnics, hikes, trips, etc. It's much better than giving your children candy.

To make it, merely wash, pit or core fruits, quarter and put in your blender and make fruit puree. (Added honey is optional.) Spread the puree about ¼ to 1/3 inch thick on saran type wrap, or anything plastic such as long clean hall runners, shower curtains, table cloths etc. Dry it in the sun from 6 to 8 hours or until pliable and leathery. If you over-dry it and it's too brittle, rejuvenate it by putting it over steam. One forgotten batch stayed out in the sun for two days (the longer it's in the sun, the more nutrition you lose), and it turned crisp. I merely took the big hall runner and gently put it over my shower door, plastic side down and turned on the hot water for just a minute. Turned off the water, shut the bathroom door, came back in about twenty minutes and it was pliable and ready to cut and roll. Leather can also be dried in the winter by a sun-filled window that reflects the sun's rays or inside a car's back window, and why not a dehydrator? Fruits may be mixed together for variety; wonderful seasonings such as cinnamon and honey is delicious with apple, tastes like applesauce, experiment, it's fun. When the leather is dry cut it in strips with scissors and roll it *with the saran* for storage. Some I cut in small 2 inch rolls and rolled without saran and put in a small plastic pail with a tight-fitting lid for snacks. It worked well. I stored fruit leather all through the house, and experimented. Rolls that I wrapped in saran and just put on a shelf dried out, so I had to steam, some flavor was lost. The rolls that were stored in a warm basement room (room temperature) turned wormy within several months. So always store it in a cool dry place in a container with a tight fitting lid and it will keep for years.

Let's Dry Vegetables

In drying vegetables, blanching or steaming before drying helps preserve vitamins, flavor, sets the color, and hastens drying by loosening cell structures. Vegetables should be shredded, diced or sliced (about ¼ inch thick). Spread food evenly on trays, don't over load (one to two pounds per tray). If you're dehydrating several foods at once, don't include onions, or other foods with strong odors. Vegetables take 4 to 12 hours, depending on the product. Fruits, 6 hours or longer. Watch carefully. (Look around your house, you might have a very warm dry place that could dehydrate food. I found a small cupboard between my refrigerator and dishwasher that is extremely warm. I can actually dry food in it. Be careful however, if it isn't warm enough your foods will spoil. Leave the door open slightly for moisture to escape. Experiment with a small quantity.

Drying test—According to the U.S. Dept. of Agriculture, food are dry when apples are pliable, springy, creamy white—apricots, pliable and leathery—berries, no visible moisture when crushed—cherries, leathery but sticky—grapes, pliable, dark brown—peaches, pliable and leathery—pears, leathery, springy feel—prunes, pliable and leathery—green lima beans, shatter when hit with hammer—snap beans, brittle, dark green to brownish—beets, brittle, dark red—carrots, parsnips, very brittle, deep orange—mushrooms, leathery to brittle—green peas, shatter when hit with a hammer—peppers and pimentos, pliable—pumpkin and squash, leathery.

Try drying some food. It's valuable experience and *know-how*, especially with predicted food shortages.

Make Some Jerky—Indian Style

Use any meat to make jerky, and trim off all fat and tendon. Slice the meat in strips no thicker than ½ inch. Remember that warm moving air dries food. So put in the sun, (that's all the indians did), in the oven or in a dehydrator. Depending on the climate the meat will dry in hours, days or weeks. The meat should be brittle and will snap easily when dry. Pack in airtight jars or wrap in heavy aluminum foil, and keep in a cool dry place. It will keep indefinitely.

Make Versatile Food Powders

You can use any dried or dehydrated meats, vegetables, fruits etc. and make wonderful food powders. Put any dried foods in your blender, a small amount at a time, and blend to a fine powder. These powders are marvelous seasonings for food. Use them instead of so much salt (see salt) and artificial flavorings. Make vegetable powders from onions, garlic, tomatoes, carrots, peas, cabbage, celery, beans, parsley and any other vegetable you can think of, put them in salt shakers, and use them in soups, stews, sauces, vegetable drinks, casseroles, main dishes, etc....Vegetable peelings (very nutritious) will dry on your cabinet. Instead of throwing them away, dry them, powder them and use them.

For fruit powders you can use any dehydrated fruits such as apples, bananas, peaches, apricots, prunes, pears, etc., or any fruit or vegetable that are not contaminated with pesticides, dyes, waxes etc. Use these fun fruit powders to make nutritious fruit syrups, gelatins, ice creams, puddings, candies, desserts and anything else you can think of. These powders are so versatile. Experiment for some family fun.

Make Your Own Bouillon

Most commercial bouillon is loaded with artificial colors, flavors and unhealthy additives such as MSG (see MSG). So make your own. Cut any meat in thin strips and dry it in the sun, oven or dehydrator (see Jerky). Blend this dehydrated meat into a fine powder for a very handy seasoning. You can use all kinds of meat for all kinds of seasonings such as beef, chicken, pork (see pork), fish, beef bacon, veal, venison etc. Go to work mothers, your creative cooking talents are just beginning. Delicious as soup, stew or gravy base. Gives meat flavor to everything.

Vegetable Tops Have Nutrition—Dry 'Em

With food prices so high, learn to use all edible food parts. Root vegetable tops are loaded with nutrition. I take carrot, radish, turnip, onion, etc., tops, wash them, dry them, chop or crush them, put them in air tight pint jars and use them in soups, stews, salads, vegetable juices, casseroles, main dishes etc. You will soon find that you won't be spending unnecessarily for commercial food flavorings. Take the strong flavored cabbage leaves around cabbage heads in your garden, and do the same. Look in your gardens and find foods that would normally go to waste and dry them, crush them and use them. Be aware that potato leaves, sprouts on potatoes, rhubarb leaves, sprouted tomato seeds, etc., are poisonous. Call the extension service and check with an agricultural agent for others that might be harmful. Don't be discouraged from using other suggested foods, however, as many of them are loaded with valuable nutrition. This knowledge might save you some future hunger pains....For easy vegetable top drying, cut a fraction off the end of the vegetable so the tops stay intact. Rinse with water and hang them on a clothes line etc. If you straddle the tops you don't have to secure them on. They will dry inside in a warm room (furnace room etc.) If you chop small amounts they will dry on a kitchen cabinet.

Storing Dehydrated Foods

Store *Home dried* foods in a dry cool place, as these foods mold easily in warm moist conditions. Some basements are too warm. Commercial dehydrated foods in sealed cans may be stored almost anywhere, but I still feel they should also be kept in a cool dry place.

Starvation Protection

Every method of preserving food causes loss of food value. But we must preserve food to survive. However, some methods are better than others. Just remember that extreme heat is the number *one* enemy of nutrition. For variety in taste, texture and food value I preserve food using every method. I dry, freeze, brine, salt, store in peat moss, can, and use any other method available.

As a wife and mother I feel a grave responsibility to my family to learn every available trick of preserving food and nutrition. When the depression and predicted food famine are a reality, my family will have a chance to survive. There is no greater security, than being knowledgeable in this area. I admonish every person to learn to be self-sufficient. The extension service, libraries, etc. are full of helpful information. We parents could stand to go hungry, but we couldn't bear to see our children starve. A hungry future is not a fanatical pipe dream; it's a reality. Start today!

Section V

Grow Your Own

Because of my husband's employment, we move often. Every new place has to have a bigger garden spot. From a 15 ft. x 20 ft. garden plot you can yield up to $350.00 worth of chemically free food. (Don't use chemicals to spray your garden. We get enough from commercial foods.) Commercial produce tastes like cardboard compared to home-grown food. From a 15 ft. x 20 ft. garden plus one foot around our back fence this year, our yield included carrots, onions, corn, beets, tomatoes, radishes, turnips, peas, string beans, spinach, lettuce, endive, garlic, parsley, chives, cucumbers, cabbage, garlic, pumpkins, sunflowers and strawberries, with summer and winter squash in our front yard.

My neighbors asked me where I got my huge plants with the beautiful yellow flowers. They soon learned about my magic eating bushes, so they plan to have food in their front yards next year. The new trend with nation-wide food shortages is—you can grow a garden anywhere. Front yard, sides, rooftops, etc.

Pick you a garden spot, then go to work. One expert says instead of worrying about depleted soil just mix good old cow manure in and that will replenish most soil depletions. Our land was solid clay; so we mixed in sand and cow manure and our yield was fantastic. When a seed package said to plant rows one foot apart, we planted 6 inches apart. We're told to give tomatoes plenty of growing room. When we put 25 tomato plants in a 15 ft. x 3 ft. spot and staked them, we were told we had overdone it. They wouldn't make it. But every plant flourished. We ate tomatoes, canned tomatoes, froze tomatoes, dried tomatoes, and you name it, tomatoes.

One little farm lady douses her plants with flour instead of chemical sprays and sells organic food by the bushel. Another takes a spray bottle, adds a little palmolive dishwashing soap (she says it's organic), dilutes it with plenty of water, sprays her plants and the bugs leave. "How do you do it, DeVona?" I asked. "How would you like to eat soap?" she replied.

Check your organic gardening books and magazines, and plant a wonderful garden. It's worth it, worth it, worth it!*

By the way, learn to preserve your garden seeds, so when the food crisis really hits, you'll be self-sufficient. Foods such as tomatoes, squash, cantaloupe, etc., have their own seeds. Keep the healthy looking ones for future planting. Other foods such as peas and beans, let them dry on the bush, then shell for planting. Other foods: radishes, lettuce, spinach, etc., if deprived of water will go to seed. Save radish pods (seeds inside) and other seedlings to plant next year. Experiment with these foods and seeds now, as food insurance for the coming food crisis. Being prepared is a great security blanket.

Inside Storage for Bulk Produce

You can insulate a north or east side basement room for produce storage (as good as a big refrigerator). You need at least one window for ventilation, shelves and removable boards on the floor. Sprinkle floor with water or wet sand or saw dust for humidity. Store vegetables in wooden crates, metal container with air holes, or lids partly off, or put root vegetables in moist sand or peat moss. Come spring put the peat moss on your garden. You can line boxes etc. with old coats, foam, wadded newspapers or any other insulation and keep onions etc., in a cold garage. One winter I just put a big old heavy blanket around a sack of onions in the garage and they kept fine. Foods must be protected from the frost but must be kept in cool temperatures. See produce storage chart.

Late crop potatoes will keep in a well ventilated cool (45 to 50 degrees F.) dark place. Lower temperatures give potatoes a sweet unappealing taste, higher temperatures cause shriveling and sprouting. Light causes a green color and destroys vitamins.

Apples keep best at 32 degrees F., and moist air. Apples shouldn't be stored with other vegetables if possible.

Peppers will keep in a perforated plastic lined box, two or three weeks at about 45 degrees F.

Sweet potatoes, squash and pumpkins can't stand outside storage so store them inside at 55 to 60 degrees. All squash (except Acorn) should be cured for storage, to keep well. To cure put in warm place (80 to 85 degrees F., furnace room) for 10 days to harden the rinds. Then store in cool place.

Also store onions in hanging perforated bags, slightly cooler than room temperature, a cool basement is excellent.

When damaging frosts come, pick tomatoes or pull tomato vines up by the roots and put in a moderately moist, cool area. Green mature tomatoes will ripen in 25 days at 55 degrees F. and in 14 days at 65 to 70 degrees F. Don't hold tomatoes at 50 degrees or below for more than a few days.

Pears should be picked mature and pale green. They ripen best after harvesting. Bartlett pears ripen immediately at 60 to 65 degrees F., while Kieffers take two to three weeks. Store pears at 32 degrees F. if possible. Pears will break down without ripening at 75 degree temperatures or above.

Outside Storage

(Pits, cellars, mounds, barrels). This method is possible if you: 1. dig vegetables for storing when soil is dry. 2. Cut tops ½ inch above crown. 3. Clean and dry them. 4. Cool them for storage.

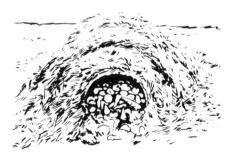

No. 1—A straw- and soil-covered barrel keeps a small quantity of vegetables or fruits.

No. 2—An underground food cellar can also serve as a storm and fallout shelter.

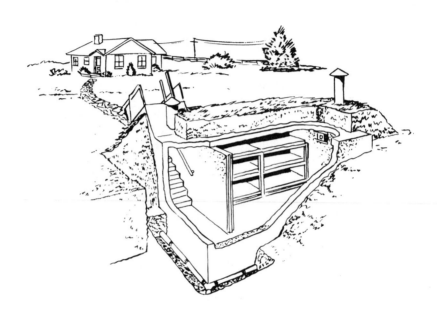

To store outside you can use: A wooden box or barrel placed on it's side, covered with straw and soil.

You can bury an old refrigerator with door upwards (would be inexpensive, because no elect icty is needed, but beware of children, a sure death trap—ren,Jve door from hinges for maximum safety). A marvelous idea however; a refrigerator that didn't work would cost next to nothing.

Underground cellars with dirt floors are excellent, as temperatures stay constant. (See illustration 2)

In *above the ground mounds* you can store pears, apples, potatoes, carrots, beets, cabbage, turnips, parsnips etc. Make a nest of bedding material such as grass, leaves, straw etc. on a well drained location. Bury small quantities of food; cover with

No. 3—Cabbages placed upright in a trench that is framed with stakes and covered with straw will keep well.

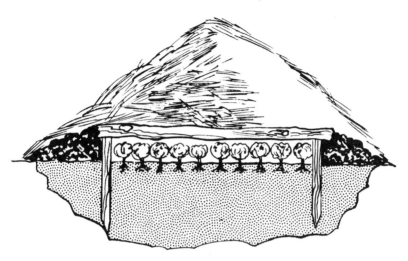

more bedding. Cover the mound with four or five inches of soil, and allow some of the bedding to come up through the mound for ventilation, then pack down firmly. Cover the bedding opening with a large board etc. to protect from rain. Dig a small ditch around the mound for drainage—pits should be rotated every year because of *left over* contamination. See illustrations 3 & 4.

The extension service has an excellent free bulletin on winter storage of foods; gives all the details. Don't hesitate to ask.

Experiment with these storage ideas; you can save hundreds of dollars by storing winter foods, and they are so nutritious, compared to commercially canned and prepackaged foods. Get the most nutrition for your money. Grow your own or go to the farms, fruit stands etc., and buy some of this wonderful natural food and put it away for winter.

Vegetables and Fruits—How We Destroy Them

How much effort do you exert to maintain a lovely home, a beautiful yard and a nice-looking car? Plenty, I'll bet. How much effort do you exert to supply yourself with valuable fuel to maintain life-long good health? Not much, really. Most people give very little thought to the foods they eat, or to their health until they lose it. We eat deprived foods, then wonder why we don't feel and function well. Take care of your most vital asset—your wonderful body.

It requires over 60 nutrients to maintain good health in the human body. Vegetables and fruits supply many of these nutrients. Once you've spent your hard-earned dollar for these foods, let them feed you—learn to preserve their food value.

Dr. W. A. Krehl of Marquette School of Medicine advises that significant amounts of critical nutrients in food are either destroyed, extracted, or discarded before they reach the consumer. Cooking, then further extracts, destroys or inactivates significant amounts of nutrients, especially vitamins.

PRODUCE STORAGE CHART

Freezing points, recommended storage conditions, and length of storage period of vegetables and fruits.

Commodity	Freezing point	Place to store
Vegetables:	o F.	
Dry beans and peas		Any cool dry place.
Late cabbage	30.4	Pit, trench, or outdoor cellar.
Cauliflower	30.3	Storage cellar.
Late celery	31.6	Pit or trench; roots in soil in storage cellar.
Endive	31.9	Roots in soil in storage cellar.
Onions	30.6	Any cool, dry place.
	30.4	Where they grew, or in storage cellar.
Peppers	30.7	Unheated basement or room.
Potatoes	30.9	Pit or in storage cellar.
Pumpkins and squashes	30.5	Home cellar or basement.
Root crops (miscellaneous)		Pit or in storage cellar.
Sweetpotatoes	29.7	Home cellar or basement
Tomatoes (mature green)	31.0	"
Fruits:		
Apples	29.0	Fruit storage cellar
Grapefruit	29.8	"
Grapes	28.1	"
Oranges	30.5	"
Pears	29.2	"

Home and Garden Bulletin No. 119, U.S. Department of Agriculture.

PRODUCE STORAGE CHART (cont.)

Commodity	Storage Conditions		Length of storage period
	Temperature	Humidity	
Vegetables:			
Dry beans and peas	32° to 40°	Dry	As long as desired.
Late cabbage	32°	Moderately moist	Through late fall and winter.
Cauliflower	"	"	6 to 8 weeks.
Late celery	"	"	Through late fall and winter.
Endive	"	"	2 to 3 months.
Onions	"	Dry	Through fall and winter.
Parsnips	"	Moist	"
Peppers	45° to 50°	Moderately moist	2 to 3 weeks.
Potatoes	35° to 40°	"	Through fall and winter.
Pumpkins and squashes	55°	Moderately dry	"
Root crops (miscellaneous)	32°	Moist	"
Sweetpotatoes	55° to 60°	Moderately dry	"
Tomatoes (mature green)	55° to 70°	"	4 to 6 weeks.
Fruits:			
Apples	32°	Moderately moist	Through fall and winter.
Grapefruit	"	"	4 to 6 weeks.
Grapes	"	"	1 to 2 months.
Oranges	"	"	4 to 6 weeks.
Pears	"	"	A few days to 3 weeks.

Other nutritional experts stress that heat and oxidation destroy over 50 per cent of food vitamins and over 75 per cent of minerals. Mothers—learn to cook nutritiously. The health of your family is in your hands!

The Food Destroyers

There are several enemies of fruits and vegetables: PROLONGED COOKING, HIGH HEAT, WATER, AIR, LIGHT, SALT, and SODA.

These are factors you have control over. Learn to use them wisely, for your family's health and dollar insurance.

If you're lucky enough to have a garden, pull only the vegetables you're going to use immediately. If you're buying from the store, buy small quantities and refrigerate immediately. Remember, up to half of the nutrients could already be lost in commercial produce so take pains to preserve what's left. We have billions of cells crying for nourishment. Feed them so they can do their job—keep us healthy.

Vegetables exposed to room temperature and light for several hours lose up to 50 per cent vitamin C, varying amounts of vitamin B 2 and folic acid.

Leafy greens have more vitamins and minerals per calorie than any other food, but their food value deteriorates rapidly.

Get the Most out of Produce

1. Buy in small quantities. Use quickly.

2. Choose the darkest and healthiest looking vegetables. Avoid pale and withered food—pick the crisp, dark green leaves and bright orange carrots, etc.

3. Buy foods in season. You have a better chance of getting local untreated food.

4. Eat produce raw whenever possible. I put platters of raw vegetables with a meal whenever possible: raw squash, green beans, peas, carrots, onions, lettuce, tomatoes, cucumbers, etc., especially during garden season. My family have learned to love raw vegetables.

5. Learn to cook nutritiously.

Avoid Produce Enemies

1. *Keep fresh produce out of light and air.* Oxygen is an enemy of vitamin A and C. Light is an enemy of vitamin B 2 (Riboflavin); it resists heat but deteriorates when exposed to light. Prepare foods rapidly for cooking and cook quickly.

2. *Water is an enemy of B vitamins.* Never soak fruits and vegetables as water-soluble vitamins leach away rapidly. Wash produce quickly, and never throw away cooking water. Drink it or use in soups, vegetable juices, etc.

3. *Don't peel food, unless absolutely necessary.* The peel on food is loaded with nutrition. Cathryn Elwood points out that the potato peel thrown out annually by the average family is equivalent in iron to 500 eggs, in protein to 60 steaks, and in vitamin C to 95 glasses of orange juice. If you must peel, never over peel; much nutrition is also just under the skin. Use a vegetable peeler rather than a knife.

4. *Never start vegetables in cold water,* and always use tiny amounts of water. Waterless cookware, inexpensive steamers (see picture) or double boilers are excellent for cooking produce. (See How to Cook Vegetables.)

5. Glass, unchipped enamel, or porcelainized iron seem to be best for cooking food. Copper destroys vitamin C on contact. Aluminum and even some stainless steel leaves metal residue in food.[14] However, many nutritionists recommend heavy stainless steel. You decide.

6. *Always use lids when cooking produce.* Open pans let in air and light and allow steam to escape. Steam is excellent as it cooks produce quickly. Pressure cookers destroy much nutrition in food. Avoid them, except for canning certain vegetables.

7. *"When you see the boil, you see the spoil,"* is my motto in cooking any food. Never let foods continually boil—always steam, or cook quickly on low heat is the secret. (Again, see Cooking Vegetables.)

8. *Never overcook food.* Cook on low heat for the shortest length of time possible. On many foods, I put on a tight lid, bring to a quick boil, take off heat (never lift lid) and let sit for about 8 to 10 minutes, then serve. If you question the safety of any foods such as green beans, etc., low boil for about 20 minutes. It's better in this case to lose nutrition than to wake up dead. (see botulism)

9. *Don't salt vegetables before or during cooking.* Always salt just before serving. Many recipes will say *add to salted water.* Be aware that spinach salted during cooking loses up to 50 per cent iron. When cooked without salt, 80 per cent was preserved. Salt used during cooking destroys nutrition. (see salt)

10. *Never add soda to cooking vegetables.* Soda destroys vitamin C and some B vitamins. Some people add soda for color retention in vegetables. Add lemon juice instead for greener greens, redder beets, and whiter whites.

How to Cook Vegetables and Fruits

We seldom cook fruits, they are so delicious eaten raw; however, if necessary, cook fruits same as vegetables. These cooking methods give maximum nutrition retention in vegetables and fruits.

Stew-In-Their-Own-Juice Method

This method is widely recommended as the best method of vegetable cookery by leading nutritionists and the British Medical Council.

Brush bottom of skillet with oil. Add thinly sliced vegetables, and add tight lid. Saute quickly on medium heat. Shake pan or stir often to prevent sticking. The steam from the natural juices, stews them in their own juices.

No Steam Sauteing

For crunchy vegetables (Chinese style) cook as above, but remove vegetables before steam tenderizes vegetables.

Steaming

There are two ways of steaming. You must have a heavy pan and tight lid for both methods. *Method one*—preheat pan. Add a couple tablespoons water. (The water turns to steam and the steam replaces the oxygen.) Add vegetables. Add tight lid. *Low heat.* Steam until tender. *Method two*—add one or two inches water in heavy pan. Put in steamer basket (see picture). Add vegetables to basket. Put lid on pan. Bring to a boil. Steam on medium heat until tender.

Double-Boiler Method

A double-boiler gives almost the same results as waterless cookware and steaming. Put one or two inches water in bottom pan. Bring to a boil. Add six or seven tablespoons water in top

Put water in the pan, and put
any basket inside pan to
steam foods.
Cooking Nutritiously

pan. Bring to boil. Add vegetables to top pan. Cover. Leave on high heat 5 or 6 seconds, so steam will replace oxygen. Put top pan on bottom pan and cook over boiling water until tender.

Broiling

Broiling gives a different flavor to vegetables. Slice vegetables thinly or cut lengthwise. Hard vegetables may be slightly precooked, then broiled. *Other method*—brush vegetables with oil. Put three inches from heat. The oil seals in the vegetable juices and nutrition. Cook rapidly at first, then turn heat low to prevent burning.

Cooking Commercially Canned Vegetables

To cook, bring juice to a boil. Add vegetables. Add lid. Take off heat and let stand couple of minutes or turn heat low until done. Commercially canned vegetables don't have botulism problems like home canned. See below.

Cooking Home Canned Vegetables and Botulism

Improperly home canned foods are principal sources of food poison—namely botulism. The toxin produced by the botulism organism is one of the most poisonous substances known. Just a tiny taste can cause death. Botulism toxin will grow only in the absence of air and in low acid foods. The poison can be present when no spoilage is evident by smell or taste. Pressure cooking when canning vegetables or preserving with strong brines or syrups will kill or inhibit the spores. If you've canned inproperly (not cleaned food well or not followed directions) low acid vegetables (some tomatoes are considered low acid) in a *water bath,* it is wise to boil gently for 20 minutes before tasting or eating as the boiling will kill the toxin—plus some nutrition, but it's better to be safe than sorry—dead sorry.

Thirty cases of botulism were reported last year in the U.S. with ten of them fatal. Many cases however, aren't reported because people think they have the flu, or doctors don't recognize the symptoms. Symptoms are: blurred and double vision, difficulty in swallowing and speaking, nausea, vomiting, abdominal pain, cramps, fullness feeling, etc. Time is critical in treatment of botulism. If suspected call—weekdays, 404-633-3311 or nights, and other times, 404-633-2176. Death usually results from paralysis of breathing.

Vegetable and Fruit Hints

—Potatoes that have frozen can be salvaged if you peel, quarter and cook them. They can be refrozen if they are cooked and mashed.

—Take surplus fresh tomatoes; wash them; slice, quarter, or leave whole and put in the freezer in plastic bags. A frozen tomato is easy to peel. Just rinse under hot water, quickly, and they can be used in salads, soups, sauces, etc.

—Basil generously planted in tomato beds will protect tomatoes.

—One average tomato gives 1800 units vitamin A and 25 mg. vitamin C.

—Some people freeze fresh green beans without blanching. Pick, wash and put in plastic bags. Fill bags with water so each bean will be in ice. Freeze. Cook ice blocked beans as fresh beans.

—A corny hint—pick fresh corn, remove from husks, wrap in freezer paper, freeze. Don't let it touch water. For eating, put cobs in a shallow baking dish, spread with butter and bake at 350 degrees for 15 to 20 minutes. Yummy!

—Quick sauerkraut—sterilize jars. Stuff each jar with shredded cabbage tightly. Use a wooden spoon for best results. Add tsp. salt and screw on lids. Emerge filled, capped jars in a tub of water. Keep them emerged or they'll explode. Change the water every three days for a week or so. When the cabbage looks like dry sauerkraut, store in a cool, dry, dark place. Eat as needed.

—Racoons eat your corn? Plant pumpkins all around your patch and they won't come near.

—Love squash? Try this...wash, take out seeds, fill cavity with pats of butter, brown sugar and pecans. Cover with foil and bake at 350 degrees for 45 minutes. Oh me, oh my.

—Is your frozen squash too soggy? Instead . . . steam it, mash it, then freeze it. It's good.

—Stuffed squash—A dear friend, Lee Benson, says cut squash lengthwise, spoon out small center. Soak bread in milk, mix with hamburger, salt and pepper. Bake covered for about 45 minutes. Last ten minutes uncover and sprinkle with grated cheese. Serve when cheese melts.

—Cook turnip tops in milk to offset the strong flavor.

—Healthy dark, bright green, crisp greens provide the greatest concentration of vitamins and minerals per calorie than any food available. They also are saturated with more insecticides, so grow and sprout your own.

—Cook vegetables while still frozen as thawing of these foods provides high nutritive losses.

—The smaller you chop your salad greens, the less nutrition. The larger the pieces, the larger nutrition. Prepare green salads just prior to serving. If exposed to air and light for any length of time they lose much nutrition. If you have to prepare salads ahead, cover immediately and put in refrigerator.

—Fruits that have thawed may be refrozen if they smell and taste good.

—Don't store onions and potatoes together. Onions hasten the spoilage of potatoes.

Crop Failure—Don't Always Blame the Weather

Crops harvested before they ripen (true of many) do not reach their maximum nutrient levels. Those shipped long distances and stored for long periods deteriorate in food value. Major mineral and vitamin losses result in the ever-increasing use of factory-processed and nutritionally-modified foods. Some chemical food additives destroy vitamins while others tie up minerals present in food and make them unavailable. Pesticides and fumigants are vitamin destroyers.[1] Because of these adulterations, the consumer receives much less for her food dollar than she realizes in buying fresh, canned, or frozen foods, because the above practices are usually prevelent in most preparations of commercial foods. These practices also put *food charts ingredients* in improper prospective. We think we're getting more than we are as far as nutrition is concerned. It's consumer deception. This information isn't told to discourage you, it's told to tell you what indeed is a reality. Read on and see what is actually done to our wonderful foods....

Part 6

Miscellaneous
Misdemeanors

Section I

Make Your Own Baby Food

Commercial baby foods are loaded with unhealthy additives and infants don't have fully developed systems to properly eliminate poisons. Baby foods are salted to please the mother's palate (see salt) and this high sodium intake is found to cause hypertension (high blood pressure) in babies,[1] and health problems in later life. Baby food needs no salting.

Sodium nitrite (see nitrites) is a common additive in baby food and nitrites cause methemoglobinemia, a condition that cuts off oxygen to the brain.[2]

Dr. Barry Commoner, Director of the Center for the Biology of the Natural Systems, University of Washington, St. Louis, Missouri, warned: *"Sufficiently concentrated dietary nitrate can lead to respiratory failure, and even death."* This evidence makes me suspicious of infant crib deaths. Could food additives be one of the culprits? European scientists blame chemical fertilizers for the excess nitrates in many foods.

MSG (monosodium glutamate) used to be a common additive in baby foods, but has been removed of late because experiments on animals showed that these animals suffered brain damage when given the same proportion of MSG contained in twenty jars of baby food.[3] The baby food manufacturers still claim that MSG is perfectly safe.[4] Who's kidding who?

Mothers—don't feel you're doing your babies a favor by loading them with commercial baby food. Feed them off the table or make your own. Put leftover food in blenders and freeze in ice cube trays or small jars. Don't over-cook these foods and make certain your baby is getting a balanced diet. A small inexpensive baby food grinder is available.* You can

---

*Happy Baby Food Grinder—Bowland-Jacobs Mfg., Spring Valley, Illinois 61362. Write for information.

quickly serve baby food right off the table. It's worth the price and there's no waste.

Sugar—A Sweet Way to Die

We're Sugared to Death

Approximately one hundred years ago, every American consumed about ten pounds of sugar per year. In 1960, the figures rose to an alarming 100 pounds per person per year. The present United States figures are horrifying. Up to 200 pounds of sugar is consumed annually by every man, woman and child. Three billion dollars a year is spent for candy.

We have conditioned our families to demand sweet in everything they eat. Breakfast cereals, beverages, canned and frozen fruits, vegetables, meats, soft drinks, cakes, cookies, ice cream, bread, rolls, candy, gum and you name it; it has to be sweet.

The Grave Digger

Parents reward, encourage and bribe their children with sweets; wives dig their husbands' graves with rich desserts and treats. No wonder sugar is one of the major contributors of heart disease.

I have a friend whose children are never without a little sack of goodies: miniature marshmallows, M & M's, chocolate chips, gum, suckers, etc. The children have white pasty faces, and this mother wonders why they refuse to eat during mealtime, and are sickly. It's evident. They are probably suffering from malnutrition, while she's proudly teaching them the ABC's.

Too Much Sugar

is Driving People Crazy

Dr. Carlton Fredricks, professor of nutrition at Fairleigh Dickinson University in New Jersey, author of the book,

Low Blood Sugar and You, warned: An enormous increase in sugar consumption is making people sick and literally driving the American public crazy. In addition to a host of physical ills, the mental problems caused from an excess of sugar in the diet include neurotic and homicidal tendencies, and feelings of rejection and anxiety. Also, at least one form of alcoholism can be directly related to an over consumption of sugar, as can learning difficulties in children and the condition known as the *tired housewife syndrome.*

Dr. Fredricks believes that, as a result, *undetected hypoglycemia* (low blood sugar) is possibly affecting as many as one of four Americans past middle age.[5]

Sugar Saps Your Energy

Sugar supplies none of the protective or body-building elements necessary to sustain life. NO VITAMINS, MINERALS, OR PROTEINS. Further, it requires greater expenditure of body energy to utilize it than the energy it produces.[6]

Refined sugar is a threat of empty calories.

Recent investigation has shown that sugar can stimulate the production of body fat in some ways apart from its calorie content in the diet. Excessive sugar consumption can adversely affect the general health, produce profound metabolic changes, cause a loss of vital energy, and be a factor in grave illnesses as coronary disease.[7]

The *refined carbohydrate* diet is blamed by Dr. Denis P. Burkitt as the single most important cause of large-bowel cancers, occurring on a world-wide scale when people forsake their traditional dietary habits and consume large amounts of *refined* carbohydrates.[8]

Avoid sugar, advises a famous English nutritionist, and you are less likely to become fat, run into nutritional deficiencies, have a heart attack, get diabetes or dental decay or a duodenal ulcer, and possibly reduce your chances of getting gout, dermatitus, and some forms of cancer, and in general increase your life span. It is important to realize that by the mere omission of a single common food and beverage ingredient such as sugar, so many benefits may result, and that its excessive use can contribute, at least in part, to so many disparate conditions and diseases.[9]

A Sweet Dilemma!!

We, the American people, are in a sweet dilemma. I used to be. I too, lived on these junk foods, until the devastating effects were felt. I would eat three or four cupcakes, then skip lunch. Now, I realize the importance of my health. Sweets moderation is vital for good health. Eat a piece of fruit instead of a candy bar. Hand your children a wedge of apple instead of a cookie.

Many people insist they don't eat a lot of sugar. Here are some surprising examples:[10]

Item	Portion	Refined Sugar
Angel food	4 ounces	7 tsp.
Cupcake, iced	1	6 tsp.
Chocolate Eclair	1	7 tsp.
Cola Drinks	6 ounce bottle	6 tsp.
Doughnut (glazed)	1	6 tsp.
Fruit Salad (canned)	½ cup	3½ tsp.
Ginger ale	6 ounces	5 tsp.
Hard candy	4 ounces	20 tsp.
Ice Cream	3½ ounces	3½ tsp.
Jelly	1 tablespoon	5 tsp.
Orangeade	8 ounces	5 tsp.
Root Beer	10 ounces	4½ tsp.
Strawberry Jam	1 tablespoon	4 tsp.

Learn to Use Honey or Molasses

For a nutritious boost in satisfying your sweet tooth learn to use honey and molasses instead of refined sugars. Honey and molasses are wonderful foods and contribute valuable nutrition (see chart). Be aware however, that molasses, honey and sugar all cause tooth decay, so rinse mouth or brush after eating these foods.

Honey's Great, Honey

Honey has been called, *Nectar of the Gods. It is hailed as a miracle healer for its ability to provide energy, to promote muscular activity, to soothe the heart, and to offer speedy assimilation directly into the bloodstream....*[11]

Honey has varying amounts of natural sugars: glucose, fructose and sucrose; dextrin, protein; calcium, copper, manganese, iron and phosphates; vitamins: thiamine, (vit. B-1), ascorbic acid (Vit. C), riboflavin, pantothentic acid, pyridoxine, and niacine, etc. However, much food value is lost in the acid filtering of commercial honey.

Honey is like marriage; the flavor improves with age. It's easy to store, and lasts indefinitely. With exorbitant rise in sugar prices, honey costs no more as a replacement for refined sugar, and look at the sweet benefits.

How to Buy, Use, and Store Honey

Honey is one of the few foods low in pesticidal contamination. Contaminated bees die before they reach the hive. Honey is also free of preservatives, artificial flavors, colors and will not mold.

For top honey value, try to buy directly from a reputable bee keeper. *Unfiltered, unheated,* or *raw* are your best buys. Honey (light or dark) that will crystallize is usually good quality.

Honey can be substituted for sugar in any recipe. Honey added to cookies, cakes, and bread doughs enhances nutrition, keeping qualities, flavor, chewiness, and gives a browner color. Honey has twice the sweetness of sugar so alter to suit your taste. When a recipe calls for sugar, I add about half the amount of honey; (e.g.) for every cup of sugar, I add only ½ cup honey. However, you might like more sweet so use ⅞ cup honey for every cup of sugar and reduce recipe liquid by 3 tablespoons for every cup of honey used, and lower oven temperature 25 degrees.

Honey will not freeze, so store it almost anywhere, in a solid container with a tight lid. If crystallized, place honey jar in pan of hot water. Don't heat very hot as flavor and nutrition changes dramatically. Also, honey that has been diluted with water will ferment.

Start today to use honey in place of sugar, it is a very valuable and nutritious food. Again, moderation in using *any* sweets.

About Molasses

Molasses is the most nutritious sweetener (see chart— more nutritious than honey) and when used moderately in cooking, adds a delicious carmel flavor to food. There are three basic kinds of molasses.

Blackstrap—This is your best molasses buy, being the waste product of sugar refinement. Much food value goes into this residue.

Unsulphured—This is your second best molasses buy. It's the juice from sunripened cane, but is a manufactured product.

Sulphured—This is your poorest molasses purchase, as sulphur is used in making sugar and it goes into this residue. Always look for Blackstrap and/or Unsulphured.

The high iron content in molasses can help cure anemia; it is also used in curing arthritis (see Wulzen Factor), plus it has many other healthful benefits.

You can substitute molasses for sugar, cup for cup (I use less molasses because of strong flavor), in any recipe, but for every cup of molasses, reduce other recipe liquid by ¼ cup. Also for best results, (if you use these food leaveners) use ½ teaspoon soda for every cup molasses added and omit baking powder (optional).

Molasses isn't mentioned often for storage as it can't be purchased in bulk. However, unopened containers will keep indefinitely in a cool, dry place. After opening, refrigerate to prevent mold. If crystalized, place jar in hot water to dissolve.

Commercial Brown Sugar
Isn't Really Brown Sugar

The commercial brown sugar color isn't from molasses residue. Raw sugar is rinsed to remove molasses residue, then put into a machine where it's separated from the crystals. This is melted, filtered and boiled repeatedly with animal-bone charcoal to concentrate and form crystals. This treatment with animal-bone charcoal gives the sugar its brown color.

Dr. W. C. Heuper, M.D. in an experimental study for *Cancer Research* warns that sugars manufactured with this animal-bone charcoal process may be carcinogenic (cancerous).[12] Make your own brown sugar; it's simple.

Homemade Brown Sugar

Blend until golden brown: 2 tablespoons molasses to every ½ cup white granulated sugar. Use your blender for best results. Store in breadbox, in a tightly covered container. If lumpy, blend in blender until free of lumps.

About Raw Sugar

The raw juice of sugar cane has over 64 food ingredients but after the manufacturers get through with it, it becomes a processed food losing much food value. Incidentally, it's far superior to white sugar, so if you have a choice use raw. However, if you have a choice between all the sweeteners, raw honey is the only sweetener that is not manufactured.

Homemade Powdered Sugar

White powdered sugar is a poor nutritional buy but if you must use it, it can be made less expensively at home.

Blend in blender to a fine powder: 1 cup sugar and 1 tablespoon cornstarch. It shouldn't feel grainy when rubbed between your fingers.

About Syrups

Even though syrup labels picture old fashioned methods of obtaining maple sap, this isn't the case with commercial syrups. Our present syrups are usually: corn syrup, granulated sugar syrup, imitation maple flavoring, carmel coloring, and salt. These syrups are almost straight refined sugar Learn to use honey or fruit puree in place of syrup, or make your own and use smaller amounts of sugar, or even gather your own. (See syrups) When buying maple syrup, look for "**100 percent** pure *untreated* maple syrup."

Head for the Hills,

and Gather Your Own Maple Syrup

Even though I have never tapped a maple tree I can't wait to try. The procedure is simple, and doesn't harm the tree. For the intermountain region, the only time to tap is in the late winter— February or March, when the sap is running heavily. Forest Service plant scientists, recommend tapping before the buds swell or you'll have an unpleasing flavor in the syrup. Also just tap trees that are seven inches or bigger. During a good flow, eight inch trees will produce up to three gallons of sap daily. Tap a lot of trees at once as it takes about 25 gallons of sap boiled to yield ½ gallon of pure maple syrup. Doesn't that sound fun? Take your family and head for the hills for a tapping good time and a cupboard full of wonderful natural syrup. (See chart for nutritional benefits.)

Sweet Equivalents:

1 cup molasses, honey, maple or corn syrup = 12 ounces
1 cup brown or raw sugar = 6 ounces
1 cup granulated sugar = 8 ounces
1 pound granulated sugar = 16 ounces (2 cups)
1 cup confectioners (powdered) sugar = 4½ ounces

Plant scientist taps into a canyon maple tree to demonstrate how to collect sap that may be boiled down into a high quality maple syrup.

COMPARATIVE NUTRITIONAL VALUES OF SWEETENERS

Food (1 lb. portions)	Refuse	Food energy	Protein	Fat	Carbo-hydrate	Cal-cium	Phos phorus
		Cal-cium	gm.	gm.	gm.	mg.	mg.
I. MOLASSES							
First extraction or light	0	1,143	–	–	295	748	204
II. HONEY							
Strained or extracted	0	1,379	1.4	0	373.3	23	27
SUGARS							
III. BEET OR CANE: Brown	0	1,692	0	0	437.3	386	86
Granual	0	1,746	0	0	451.3	0	0
Powder	0	1,746	0	0	451.3	0	0
IV. MAPLE SYRUP							
(Not commercial)	0	1,579	–	–	408	649	50

About Artificial Sweeteners

Four non-nutritive sweeteners, now banned, are the cyclamates (or cyclohexylsulfamates)—calcium, magnesium, potatasium and sodium cyclamates. Three others are ammonium saccahrin, calcium saccharin and sodium saccharin. Two more for special dietary supplements: sorbital, which also has many other uses, and rylital.[13]

Saccharin

They banned cyclamates because they were proven to cause cancer; Saccharin also produces cancer.

The cyclamate ban prompted a long overdue review of saccharin. A saccharin pellet-implant technique induced bladder cancer in about half the treated mice. In another study, three out of twenty male rats fed saccharin in their diet for two years developed bladder tumors that *appeared to be malignant.*[14]

Sweet News—The Sweet Berry

Hey dieters, don't give up on low-calorie sweeteners. Cyclamates and saccharin etc., do have definite health problems, but the frantic search of the diet-food industry has found a natural low-calorie sweetener from a berry growing

COMPARATIVE NUTRITIONAL VALUES OF SWEETENERS

Iron	Sodium	Potassium	Vitamin A	Riboflavin	Niacin	Thiamine	Ascorbic Acid
mg.	mg.	mg.	Int. units	mg.	mg.	mg.	mg.
I. 19.5	68	4,160	–	.27	.9	.32	–
II. 2.3	23	231	0	.20	1.2	.02	5
III. 15.4	136	1,560	0	.15	.8	.05	0
.5	5	14	0	0	0	0	0
.5	5	14	0	0	0	0	0
IV. 6.4	64	1,098	–	–	–	–	0

Above material researched in USDA Agriculture Handbook no. 8.

wild in tropical West Africa, known as the wild red berry or the serendipity berry. This fruit is 3,000 times sweeter than sugar. Researcher Dr. James A. Morris isolated the sweet from the berry named Monellin. It's so sweet that *one 400th of an ounce dissolved in a glass of water imports a definite sweet sensation to the tongue. Another plus, Monellin is a protein. This berry is now under study for human consumption.*

Chew Your Heart Out—

Chewing Gum is Plastic, Petroleum, Coal Tars.

From one gum chewer to another, I am just as annoyed as you must be to learn that the *mad manufacturers could put such harmful products on the market for us to eat....Eat gum? Absolutely. Two-thirds of every stick of gum we chew is actually swallowed, along with the 25 suspicious ingredients that don't even have to appear on the label.*

Consumer Bulletin points out that periodic shipments of chewing gum bases have been seized because of contaminated insect and rodent filth, or had unallowed coal-tar colors[15] (carcinogenic).

The familiar plastic polyethylene (used in making children's toys) is an approved plasticizer in chewing gum! BHA, BHT and propylgallate derived from petroleum and coal tars, are added to prevent the gum from going stale. Phenethyl benzoate is added to give a fruit or honey flavor.[16] And this is just an eye opener. There's much more.

So you realize that sugared gum not only destroys teeth (each stick is 60 percent sugar), the non sugared gums with artificial sweetners (saccharin) are suspected carcinogenics (cancer-inciters), not to mention gum chewing fills our digestive system with plastic, derivatives of petroleum, and coal tars.[17] No wonder we're a sickly nation; not to mention our poor children.

I'm very concerned about the children, as many of these dangerous additives are also present in commercial candies and treats.

Chocolate Lovers' Dilemma

You chocolate lovers should be aware that chocolate and cocoa interfere with calcium assimilation in the body. When you serve your families hot chocolate, chocolate milk, and other chocolate goodies, you're depriving their bones, teeth etc.

No one is more sorry than I, to learn that chocolate is a detrimental food, but had I learned it sooner, possibly I wouldn't have my life savings invested in my mouth. If you have a difficult time giving up this tasty calcium-killer, then do what we do at our house, indulge only on rare occasions, and use Carob and Pero (marvelous nutritious chocolate substitutes) instead. Carob and Pero are available at most grocery stores and health food outlets. Pero (coffee flavor) gives Carob a rich chocolate flavor.

Chocolate Substitutes

(3 tablespoons Carob and 3 tablespoons Pero with 4 tablespoons water equal 1 square chocolate. Or susbtitute the Carob/Pero powder cup for cup for cocoa.) Try this Carob/Pero recipe. Don't tell your family it's not chocolate. Many times they won't eat if they know you've made a change. (See *Eating What Comes Naturally* for Carob/Pero recipes.)

Pretend Hot Chocolate

This is a very nutritious drink.

1 quart water and 1 cup regular powdered milk (1 1/3 cups instant) Make a paste and add to the reconstituted m.lk using 4 tablespoons Carob, 4 tablespoons Pero, 3 tablespoons brown sugar, 4 tablespoons water and 1 teaspoon vanilla. Heat and serve. Delicious topped with whipped cream.

Section III

Make 'Em Easy Gelatins

Commercial gelatins are mostly sugar, water and additives. Homemade gelatins take as much effort to make as opening a gelatin box. Unflavored gelatin is the secret. So keep plenty on hand and put some in storage.

Just remember that 1 package (1 tbsp.) unflavored gelatin will jell two cups of any liquid:*fruit or vegetable juices, liquified fresh or dried fruit, sweetened fruit powder juice, thawed (frozen) fruit cubes etc. (If you have commercial gelatin on hand, make it; then make the *Basic Homemade Gelatin and mix them together. This will at least dilute the sugar and additives.*

Basic Homemade Gelatin

*1 pkg. unflavored gelatin
2 cups fruit juice*

Sprinkle gelatin over ½ cup cold juice without stirring. Let stand 10 or more minutes. Heat slowly until gelatin is dissolved. Pour heated mixture into rest of juice, stirring. Add sliced fruits; shredded carrots, cabbage, etc., if desired. Refrigerate.

Quick Gelatin

Sprinkle 1 pkg. unflavored gelatin over 1 cup cold juice, without stirring. Wait 10 minutes. Heat softened gelatin mixture slowly to dissolve. Stir 8 to 10 frozen fruit cubes (see fruit cubes) in hot mixture until cubes are dissolved. Refrigerate for 30 minutes or until set.

*Fresh pineapple or it's juice will not jell; bring to a boil first, then cool.

chopped onion, green pepper and any other vegetables or seasonings to taste. Simmer until vegetables are soft. Dissolve gelatin in hot mixture. Pour in mold and refrigerate until firm. Unmold on small platter and garnish.

Experimenting With Gelatin is Great Fun

Unflavored gelatin is so versatile. It can be used to make gelatins, aspics, process cheese, economical salad dressings etc. Experiment and come up with 1,000 more uses. Just remember that 1 pkg. of unflavored gelatin will jell 2 cups of any liquid. (For more solid molds use 1½ to 1¾ cups liquid.)

Section IV

The Nuts Who Process Our Nuts

Nuts in the natural state are wonderful foods and very pleasing to the palate, but here's what the *nuts* do to our wonderful nuts.

Walnuts may be bleached in a chloride of lime and sodium carbonate solution to give them a uniform color. English walnuts shells may be loosened by ethylene gas. Many nuts are fumigated by methyl bromide to keep the insects away. Then walnuts and pecans are usually dipped in hot lye and rinsed in acid; or into a solution of glycerine and sodium carbonate then dipped in citric acid. Pistachios are often dyed bright red and heavily crusted with salt.[18]

In Consumer Bulletin Annual, *Foods and Nutrition,* 1962-63, it explains that our *roasted* nuts are not roasted at all. They are usually deep-fried in heated and reheated oils. Heated and reheated oils are carcinogenic. This high heat destroys three-fourths of the thiamine and much vitamin E.

Other nuts are doctored with BHA, BHT, acetylated monoglyceride, and are sprayed heavily with pesticides. Pesticides concentrate in fatty foods.

Problem Peanuts

Peanuts can definitely be a problem because of Aspergillis flavus, an aflatoxin mold. Researchers believe this mold may be the culprit in spreading liver disease among humans and animals in the tropics. This toxin can kill turkeys, ducklings, pigs, calves, etc. And cows can pass the toxin through milk. *Aspergillis flavus* have been termed "the most powerful hepatic (liver) carcinogens known."[19] Some commercial peanut butter was quietly recalled when found to be contaminated with this poison. Just watch for fuzz. Fuzzy (moldy) nuts shouldn't be eaten. Check raw peanuts especially.

Those Health Nuts

Famed nutritionist LeLord Kordel points out that peanuts and almonds are rich sources of protein, B vitamins, calcium, phosphorus and iron. They contain nearly 26 percent linoleic acid, one of the essential fatty acids necessary to help control cholesterol metabolism.[20] However, some of the added oils and shortenings in commercial peanut butter are contributors to cholesterol, so make your own. (See homemade Peanut Butter)

Walnuts are good sources of the desirable polyunsaturated fatty acids, and low in saturated ones. Pecans are also fairly favorable in their polyunsaturated fat content. The oil in cashews is like milk fat, and contributes to cholesterol.[21]

How to Buy Nuts

Raw nuts, nuts in the shell and vacuum-tinned, shelled, uncoated nuts are your best buys. Unskinned peanuts are higher in thiamin, so eat the skins. Read labels for additives, hopefully they'll be listed.

After opening cans or cracking nuts, be sure and refrigerate or freeze to insure against rancidity. If mold is evident on nuts, wheat, corn, soybeans, rice, cottonseed, and other grains, discard to protect humans and animals. Raw peanuts store very well in a cool, dry place.

Peanut Butter
How Nutritious Really?

Peanut butter made from lightly roasted or raw peanuts is a desirable food for children and adults alike. It provides reasonably good-quality protein, differing amounts of vitamins and highly desirable unsaturated fatty acids. The commercial brands that say, "peanuts and salt, that's all" are good peanut butter buys. But most commercial peanut butter has hydrogenated vegetable oil, dextrose, salt, emulsifiers (monoglycerides and diglycerides), artificial flavorings, texturizers, color additives, chemical preservatives and anything else that will make the product *appealing*. These adulterations don't coincide with nature. They work against natural body functions, so make it yourself by turning on your blender.

Homemade Peanut Butter

Put raw or lightly roasted peanuts in blender (any amount). Add salt to taste if peanuts aren't already salted. Drizzle in tiny amounts of vegetable oil until you get desired consistency. All peanut butter should be stored in refrigerator. (This won't cost any less than commercial brands, but by feeding your family wholesome nutritious foods, you will see a change in your doctor bills....Just one fringe benefit.)

Section VI

For Popcorn Lovers Only

One half cup popping corn equals approximately one quart popcorn; so if you're a popcorn lover put some in storage.

Good popping corn has the right moisture content, and pops easily. Older corn is difficult to pop, but don't despair, and don't be afraid to store some because you can put the *pop* back in the corn. Old corn has just lost its moisture, so to rejuvenate it, give the kernels a good stiff shot—of water. Put about a half cup old corn kernels and two tablespoons water in a closed jar and shake to moisten the kernels. Let it stand several days. Presto! It's ready to do a popping good job.

Section VII

Those Soft Drinks Are Shortening Your Life

(When you're thirsty, drink water instead.)

Many children are suffering from malnutrition because of unaware parents. Adults load their children with sweets and junk foods, especially soft drinks. I've actually seen toddlers drinking coke from baby bottles. Those FOOLISH, FOOLISH MOTHERS. Adults should take note, as the ravaging effects of soft drinks are being felt in the U. S. and abroad.

Modern Nutrition reported, November 1965, that 243 eight-ounce bottles of soda water were consumed annually by every man, woman and child. Imagine what the figures are now, with sales doubling every year since the low-calorie soft drink boom.

Look Ma! Everybody is a Gummer

Nutritionists Dr. Clive McKay and his associates in experiments with soft drinks, dropped extracted human teeth in cola drinks. Within two days the teeth became extremely soft, with loss of much calcium off the enamel surface. Well fed rats given only cola beverages to drink had their molar teeth dissolved down to the gum line after six months.

—When Dr. McKay reported the rat experiments to the *Hearings before the House Select Committee to Investigate the Use of Chemicals in Food Products*, he was informed that the soft-drink industry's massive economic investments were important and a representative suggested that Dr. McKay's shocking findings be given a soft-touch to keep from disrupting the industry and economy. Dr. McKay retorted, that the health of our children just might be as important as the welfare of the soft-drink industry.[22]

Dr. McKay also emphasized concerning the exceeding amount of phosphoric acid in *pop,* especially in cola drinks. The strong acid is masked by the exorbitant amount of sweeteners. He also pointed out when we're drinking cola beverages we are drinking a mixture of phosphoric acid, sugar, caffeine, coloring, and flavoring matter.

An excessive quantity of phosphorus can upset the body's calcium-phosphorus balance. Plus evidence points to iron deficiency with high phosphate consumption, as the iron cannot be absorbed properly. Acids (acetic, citric, lactic, and phorphoric) and sodium acetate, pyrophosphates, hydroxides or carbonates of sodium are the sources of acid in these drinks.

Deadly Caffeine

Caffeine affects the heart in that as little as one cup of coffee elevates the pulse and systalic blood pressure. Large amounts may cause irregularities of the heart beat. These beverages may increase the risk of heart trouble. This is especially true where people drink five or more cups a day. Caffeine stimulates the secretion of gastric acids and enzyme production. Large amounts of caffeine also tends to raise the blood sugar in diabetics. Habitual coffee drinkers may experience headache, 18 hours after being deprived. Bad effects of caffeine are nervousness, tremor, palpitation, insomnia, headache, and digestive disorders.

The deadly effects of caffeine are coming to light as researchers have reported, *"There is a strong likelihood that caffeine may prove to be one of the most dangerous mutagens in man."*[23] Caffeine crosses the placental barrier and its effects on the fetus are under study. It's on the FDA list of additives to be studied for safety,[24] while Americans drink it by the gallon.

Diethyl pyrocarbonate also known as pyrocarbonic acid diethyl ester (DEP) is another official inciter of cancer. It is used in noncarbonated soft drinks, fruit-based beverages (fruit drinks, ades, nectars, and punch).[25]

Ethylenediaminetetracetic (wow) acid and other chemicals are used to *separate out-of-the-way* traces of chemicals that might otherwise interfere with chemical processing. They're called *sequestrants,* and are used in frozen fruits, soup bases, process cheese, evaporated milk, vinegar, soft drinks, and other products.[26]

These problems mentioned only touch the soft drink menace. Most *pop* ingredients are harmful materials not meant for man to take internally. When you're thirsty, take a drink of water. Use soft drinks only sparingly. Instead of filling your refrigerator and cupboard with junk foods, use your grocery money for food that will make you, as Cathryn Elwood says *Feel Like a Million.*

Your Own Home Brew

If you must have soft drinks, here are some recipes to brew at home (remember that homemade soft drinks are mostly sugar-see sugar.)

Homemade Root Beer

Makes about 33 - 12 ounce bottles
1 package Hires Root Beer Extract
4 cups white granulated sugar
3 gallons tepid water
½ teaspoon all purpose wine yeast, champagne yeast, or brewers yeast.

Cherry Pop Fizz

Makes about 26 - 12 ounce bottles
2 ounces cherry extract
2½ gallons (10 quarts) warm water
6 heaping cups white granulated sugar
½ teaspoon all purpose wine yeast

Soft Drink Instructions

Pour sugar, water and extract (shake extract well) into a large clean plastic bucket. Stir thoroughly. Sprinkle yeast over mixture, let sit a moment, then stir thoroughly with long wooden spoon. Stir until yeast dissolves TOTALLY. Funnel beverage into strong bottles to ½ inch of top. Cap and store as below.

Pop Hints:

—Use only strong returnable pop bottles. Non-returnables can explode. Use a crown capping machine or tight-fitting plastic caps. Store crown cap bottles on side; plastic capped bottles upright in a well padded box. Store at 70 degrees for five days; 80 degrees for one or two days—refrigerate when done.

What You Should Know About Oils

Almost all commercial cooking oils are highly refined, stripping this food of its life-giving value. Refined oil is treated with caustic soda, lye or other strong alkalis. When oil is extracted, the seeds etc., are crushed and heated with a light petroleum fraction (gasoline) solvent. This dissolves the oil.

Much, much more is done to our wonderful natural oils, but let's merely point out that when it reaches the grocery shelf it's a very depleted food...namely, the valuable substances that lower cholesterol are removed. Among these, vitamin E.

Freshly pressed crude vegetable oils in dark containers, are your best buys, but aren't very appealing. Cold pressed oils—corn, peanut, olive, soy, sesame and safflower are good (health food store). Some olive oils are good, with *Genuine Imported Virgin Oil* as best. *Pure olive oil* is a highly refined product, but take note that any olive oil gives off a sweet unappealing odor when heated.

Some oil manufacturers are now listing on labels, *no chemicals—no preservatives—will cloud when refrigerated, etc.* These are better commercial buys. Avoid cottonseed oil—loaded with pesticides, and coconut oils—extremely high in saturated fats. Reheated oils and oils in prolonged heat (commercial deep fat fryers), have proven to be a carcinogenic. Avoid them. Doughnuts, potato chips, some bakery goods, heat and serve foods, etc., are usually cooked with reheated oils.

Mineral Oil—Don't Use It!

The FDA warns that we should not consume mineral oil, but yet you'll find this as a listed ingredient on many product labels. Mineral oils interferes with vitamin absorption in the body, and is suspected of being a carcinogenic.

Consumer Bulletin reports that physicians at John Hopkins Hospital are concerned about the amount of mineral oil found in the lymph nodes and other tissues of persons examined. They suspect that mineral oil might be the culprit in mysteriously damaged tissues.[27]

Many people today still use mineral oil as a laxative, inspite of warnings from physicians. Adele Davis warned of the possible dangers of this oil even in cold creams, baby oil, and cosmetics.[28] Avoid it, and avoid the products that list it as an ingredient.

Shortening—A No No!

You can't believe what you are eating when you eat shortening-filled foods unless you could see the pages and pages of research. However, I have two short paragraphs to encourage you to stay away from this highly objectionable product. Shortening is a hydrogenated product, that works against natural body processes, altering lecithin, a natural cholesterol fighter. Always use unrefined oils instead of shortening (see margarine). You can substitute these products cup for cup, but for excellence, it is recommended to use recipes devised for the different oils. I interchange always and get good results. You decide.

If you have shortening in storage and are determined to use it; use it to grease your bread pans, etc., rather than adding it to a recipe, then dust your pans with whole wheat flour. Most of the floured shortening will stay in the pan or can be brushed off your baked product.

What About Lard?

Old fashioned *pure lard is a saturated fat taken from pork. (See Pork). If the label doesn't stress the pure* factor, avoid it, as it is hydrogenated, bleached, filtered and full of antitoxins just as shortening. Pure lard will melt at room temperature and has to be refrigerated. Most lards today will merely sit in the kitchen cupboard, like shortening, and not deteriorate, because it's not food. Real food molds, spoils, and deteriorates.

Make 'Em Easy Condiments

We are a catsup, mustard, mayonnaise, salad dressing eating people. Most condiments have no labeling, but they are loaded with dangerous additives, emulsifiers, thickeners, softening agents, and anything else for consumer appeal. These foods are simple to make at home:

Mayonnaise or Salad Dressing Hints

Mayonnaise and salad dressing making is as simple as turning on your blender. Just remember, in making various amounts to use approximatley 1 cup oil for every egg (add extra egg yolks for extra richness, if desired.) Never add oil too quickly as the egg won't absorb it. Always drizzle oil in pencil stream for proper emulsion. When oil starts to appear on top of emulsion, you've added enougn. (If you prefer commercial condiments, mix them. Half commercial, half homemade.)

Rich Mayonnaise or Salad Dressing

2 eggs
2 cups oil
1 or 2 teaspoons dry mustard ⎱ *2 makes it tart.*
1 or 2 tablespoons vinegar ⎰
    (cider vinegar best)
garlic, seasoning, or regular salt to taste

Blend eggs, mustard, vinegar and seasonings until frothy. Leave blender on and drizzle oil in a pencil stream until all oil is emulsified. Ready to eat. Keep refrigerated.

Economical Mayonnaise or Salad Dressing

1 package unflavored gelatin in ½ cup cold water
1 cup water

½ cup powdered milk
2 eggs
1 cup oil
1 tablespoon dry mustard
3 tablespoons vinegar or dill pickle juice
1½ teaspoons salt
Add to taste any (garlic, parsley, dill, tarragon, thyme, oregano, basil, seasoning salts, etc.)

Soften gelatin for 5 to 10 minutes in ½ cup cold water; heat to dissolve, then cool. Put eggs, mustard, vinegar, salt and seasonings in blender. Whip until frothy. Add cooled gelatin. Leave blender on, drizzle oil in pencil stream for emulsion. Ready to eat. Refrigerate.
Always keep homemade or commercial condiments in refrigerator.

Thousand Island Dressing

Add to taste:
chopped olives, any chopped pickles, pimento, chopped onion, chili sauce, chopped green pepper to homemade mayonnaise.

French Dressing

½ cup cider vinegar
1½ cups oil
1 teaspoon dry mustard
1 teaspoon garlic salt or 1 teaspoon salt with ½ clove minced garlic
½ teaspoon pepper
½ teaspoon paprika

Combine all ingredients in jar with tight lid. Shake well. Refrigerate. Best to let sit at room temperature for 10 or 15 minutes before serving. Shake well again before serving.

Homemade Mustard

¼ cup mustard seed
½ cup vinegar
½ cup water
2 tablespoons flour
½ teaspoon salt
2 teaspoons sugar

¼ teaspoon celery seed
⅛ teaspoon tumeric
¼ teaspoon nutmeg

Add mustard seeds to blender. Blend to break seeds. Add vinegar and water and blend into smooth puree. Put puree in heavy pan and add other ingredients. Cook very slowly, stirring constantly until thick and smooth. (Burns easily, so watch it.) Put in jar, cover and refrigerate.

Homemade Catsup

½ cup vinegar
1 teaspoon celery seed
1 teaspoon whole cloves
1 teaspoon crushed cinnamon stick
12 red-very ripe tomatoes
1 cup water
½ cup minced onion (if using dehydrated, re-constitute first)
dash pepper
2 teaspoons salt
1/3 cup sugar

Boil first four ingredients for one minute. Set aside. Puree tomatoes and onion in blender, then bring to slow boil. Add water, and pepper. Bring to boiling point; lower heat, add sugar and simmer until medium thick. Strain to remove seeds (optional). Strain vinegar mixture, add to puree and simmer until desired thickness. Refrigerate for use or put in sterile bottles and seal or freeze.

Economic Tomato Peel Catsup

Use peels when canning tomatoes.
Put clean tomato peels, stems, cores in blender. Add a little water and blend until smooth.
For every 2 quarts of blended peel, use 1 cup vinegar, 1 onion, 1 garlic cube, salt, pepper and brown sugar to taste. Cook on medium heat until curled peel floats to top. Put through colander to remove peel. Cook slowly to desired thickness. Eat, or bottle and seal or freeze.

About Canned Soups

Here are the ingredients of a popular brand of Cream of Mushroom soup: water, mushrooms, wheat flour, soy oil, non-fat dry milk, salt, food starch-modified, vegetable oil base mix (partially hydrogenated soy oil, lactose, sodium caseinate, dipotassium phosphate), tomatoes, hydrolyzed vegetable protein, sugar, monosodium glutamate, spice, natural flavoring, cream, ascorbic acid (vitamin C) added to protect color, onion powder, garlic powder, oleoresin paprika.

Another popular brand doesn't list ingredients. For example, they merely put (tomato soup): prepared from: tomatoes, enriched wheat flour, sugar, salt, vegetable oil, natural spice oils and vitamin C....We realize this soup is prepared from these above ingredients. But what I'd like to know is, what are the other ingredients? This type of labeling doesn't inform us.

Most commercial products including canned soups have monosodium glutamate. You'll also find this additive in condiments, pickles, meats, candy, baked goods and Chinese foods, etc. Monosodium glutamate causes brain damage in animals; and headaches, chest pain and numbness in humans.

Homemade soups aren't as convenient as opening a can, but they are easy, delicious and nutritious.

Homemade Cream of Mushroom Soup

¼ lb. fresh mushrooms, chopped
½ onion, minced
2 tbsp. butter
⅛ c. w.w. flour
¼ tsp. salt
Dash pepper
Dash nutmeg
1 1/3 c. chicken bouillon (homemade)
½ cup light cream

Saute mushrooms and onion in butter for 10 minutes. Stir in flour and seasonings until smooth paste. Slowly add bouillon, slowly, stirring. Bring mixture to a boil, stirring constantly. Reduce heat, cover and simmer 6 or 7 minutes. Add cream. Heat slowly. Serve. 3 to 4 servings.

Easy Chicken Noodle Soup

Cook noodles until done, rinse and drain. Make chicken bouillon (1½ tsp. per 8 oz. cup water) Add noodles, leftover diced chicken, minced onion tops etc., to bouillon. Heat and serve.

Easy Vegetable Soup

Dice onions, celery, carrots, potatoes, green pepper etc., or use dehydrated vegetables and simmer slowly until tender. Add leftover roast beef, stew meat, etc., and beef bouillon (1½ tsp. bouillon to 8 oz. cup water.) Use as much bouillon as desired. Mix all together. Heat, season and serve.

Note—Some bouillon also has monosodium glutamate, check the labels.

Prepackaged Dinners—Very Poor Food Buys

It's well known when foods are cooked then reheated, food value is lost. Because of this, *heat and serve-* type meals are very poor food buys, as they have been precooked before you heat them. This is a good example of *filling* your family, but not *feeding* them.

Frozen dinners are especially unhealthy buys because this food can be frozen and thawed many times before reaching the grocer, let alone your table. Bacteria counts were in the millions on some of these dinners. Avoid this type of food.

Another example—Beef Stroganoff is required, by food standard, to have 45 percent meat, the rest being noodles, garnish and sour cream. A test on a popular brand contained only 20 percent beef rather than the 45 percent claimed on the label. Spend your money on foods that will nourish you. Most prepackaged meals just don't do the job.

Those Dirty Spices

Commercial imported spices contain a lot of unbelievable ingredients. Various imported spices are allowed to contain between 0.5 and 2 percent, by weight, of extraneous matter, such as stones, dirt, wire, string, insect parts and animal hair. A FDA official reported that spices produced in this country, such as basil and tarragon, are not checked for extraneous matter unless they have been processed or stored in unclean facilities.   Can you imagine what's in them? Spices can be grown in gardens during summer, on window sills during winter; dry them and put in jars. (See sausage—food powders etc.)

(By)—Pass the Salt

Out of habit, Americans salt their foods with a heavy hand. Present salty advice is—we'd better *shake lightly.* Nutritionists warn that mother nature has added enough natural sodium to foods and additional salt isn't necessary. But because we shun most *words of wisdom* be informed that we consume up to 20 times more salt than the body needs and can utilize properly. For example, potato chips have up to 341 times more sodium as a raw potato of the same weight. There's added salt in almost everything we buy, then we add more salt in cooking, then again at the table; even commercial drinks and medicines are heavily salted. It is proven the more salt we eat, the more we crave; the less we eat, the less we crave. Try changing your salty habit, as over-consumption of this food is very detrimental to health.

Aware physicians are sounding the alarm, as excessive salt is causing some hazardous health problems including heart disease, atherosclerosis, high blood pressure, hypertension and obesity. Baldness, tooth decay, sleeplessness and other unexplained ailments are also suspected. Some highly salted foods are blamed for obesity moreso than the actual foods eaten....So when you grab for the shaker, remember to shake gently for your health's sake. Also, people living inland should use *iodized salt* because our diets are lacking in iodine, however, with the above precautions. Avoid salt substitutes as they are not healthful products.

About Pepper

The most common pepper is black pepper, popular with American cooks. White pepper is a mild pepper while cayenne is extremely hot and biting. Pepper all foods lightly, as too much pepper inflames the stomach.

About Food Leavenings

It's well known that baking powder and soda used in cooking aren't suitable foods. But we use them out of habit. Low-sodium baking powders can be obtained at a health food store or try adapting your recipes by using yeast or extra egg whites for leavening purposes and omit baking powder and soda. Use 1 tsp. yeast for light cakes. Up to 3 tbsp. for cakes with heavy ingredients. Dissolve yeast for 10 to 15 minutes in any recipe liquid that has been warmed.

About Baking Powder

Because we use baking powders let me remind you that baking powder is an acid and alkaline material put together.

When moisture is added they form a carbon dioxide gas causing tiny air bubbles in your batters. The heat quickly sets the batter, making a light airy product. Moisture in cupboards and storage areas can cause baking powder to lose potency. So keep it air tight and dry. If you want to check it's potency, put a heaping teaspoon baking powder in ½ cup hot water. If the product is good, it will bubble to beat the band. If it doesn't throw it out.

Homemade Baking Powder

This recipe will not store well, so make enough for only immediate use.

For every 2 cups flour in recipe:

Use and mix...1 tsp. salt, 4 tsp. cream of tarter, and 2 tsp. bicarbonate of soda.

Baking Soda (Bicarbonate of Soda)

Baking soda is used in a recipe when sour milk, honey, molasses, etc., are present, giving a tender crumb. (See About Food Leavenings) Remember, however, that soda destroys nutrition, so you decide. If you're still determined to use it, knowning what you do, in making-up your own recipes you can use ½ tsp. soda and ½ tsp. baking powder for every 2 cups flour. The soda neutralizes the acid, and the leavening action is taken care of by the baking powder.

About Water

Water that contains certain minerals and is relatively *hard,* rather than *pure* and *soft,* gives you some assurance of better teeth, with less decay; and what is more important, a decreased liklihood of dying of heart disease.[29] So as far as health is concerned, hard water is best. Hook your soft water to the hot water tap only. Never to your drinking water.

For maximum benefits in drinking water, we are advised to drink liquids between meals, or 15 minutes before mealtime if possible. Drinking excessive amounts of liquid during meals and especially drinking while chewing food dilutes digestive juices. Some experts claim when digestive juices are diluted, some of our food will actually spoil in our stomachs and not be properly utilized by the body. Sour stomachs, anyone?

Coffee, Tea, and Other Caffeine Related Foods

The FDA's *fact sheet* list, says that: cola's contain from 40 to 72 m.g. per twelve-ounce serving. One cup of coffee or tea about 90 m.g. caffeine. Then Hershey points out that one ounce of bitter chocolate contains 25 m.g. One ounce cocoa, 50 m.g., a one-ounce bar of milk chocolate, 3 m.g. Pills to make you stay awake, 112 m.g. People gorge themselves with the above stimulants, then load themselves with tranquilizers to unwind.

Since most Americans are coffee drinking people, be aware that caffeine increases the production of stomach acid and probably contributes to the number of misery of persons suffering from peptic ulcers.[30]

Experiments on animals have shown that caffeine caused birth defects. It is recommended that women in the first three months of pregnancy should reduce or totally eliminate their intake of caffeine-containing beverages, foods and drugs.[31] (Also see caffeine—soft drinks)

What You Should Know About Vinegars

There are tangy, rich or mild vinegars, and they definitely alter the taste of a recipe. Vinegars are usually used to pickle, to marinate and to make dressings etc., but let's not forget that all vinegars are corrosive, so always use stainless, glass or enamel utensils when vinegar is used. Stay away from iron ware, copper, zinc. or galvanized containers. There are several different vinegars:

Cider Vinegar (Also Malt Base Vinegar)

The natural apple cider vinegar is the best vinegar for your food dollar. It contains valuable digestive ferments which you won't find in white distilled vinegar. Some naturalists claim when cider vinegar is added to honey, it can cure many ills and possibly they are right. Cider vinegar is between 50 to 60 percent acetic acid.

White Distilled Vinegar

White distilled vinegar is used when pickled foods are to remain light in color. However, I wonder if the light color is worth it, as this vinegar is 40 percent acetic acid count or grain, based on chemicals.

Herb Vinegars

Herb vinegars can be made from any vinegar. Garlic vinegar is made by crushing a garlic bud and leaving it in the vinegar from 20 to 24 hours. Other herbs, use 1 tsp. herbs, or more, to 1 1/3 cup vinegar and let it steep (soak) for 4 weeks. Strain it, put in sterilized containers and cork tightly.

About Homemade Cider Vinegars

In making your own vinegars, you should become acquainted with the word *mother*. *Mother* in vinegar making is the unappealing film composed of bacteria and yeast cells that form on the surface of fermenting liquids and is especially active in the production of vinegars. Also called *mother of vinegars*. *Mother* is like a sour dough starter; it expedites the process in making quick vinegars.

Homemade Apple Cider Vinegar

Wash, peel, and cube tart apples, saving the skins, cores and stems. Put in blender and puree or put through a potato ricer, saving the juice. Pour puree into a cloth (muslin or an old clean pillow case) and catch the juice. Pour juice into clean dark (cover jars if not dark) glass jars or jugs. Rubber band several thickness of cheesecloth over top, and put in a cool dark place for 6 months. Strain, put in sterile bottles and cork.

Apple Core Cider

Put cores, stems, peelings and overripe or bruised apples in a large jar. Cover these with cold water and put in a warm place. Add more apple wastes every so often. When vinegar strength suits you, strain, bottle and cork. Save the *mother* to make future batches.

Quick Cider Vinegar

Sweet apple cider placed in a warm place for several weeks will turn to hard cider (vinegar). For even faster results add some *mother* to sweet cider, then put in warm place.

Vinegar Stetcher

When half your sweet cider is gone, fill the rest of the jug with water; add 1 cup brown sugar, (white will also work,) then let ferment. The sugar replaces the diluted acid.

Are Irradiated Foods Dangerous?

Sources of radiation are termed *food additives* under American law. The FDA presently disapproves of this type of preservative. Irradiated foods change drastically inasmuch as irradiated potatoes won't sprout, and irradiated pork doesn't spoil readily.

X-ray (ionized radiation) destroys important ingredients in food. Exposure to x-rays can cause sterility and cancer in humans and animals. There is now fear that eating irradiated foods could also cause cancer in humans.

In Selecting Vitamins

Although the FDA denies that any differences exist between vitamins from natural and synthetic sources, real difference, and in some instances, very significant ones do exist. Reading the label is most important. Some vitamins that say *natural* may come from only 10 percent natural foods. Check your source carefully.

Part 7

How to Change
Your Eating Habits
and How to Find
"Help" and "Happiness"

How to Change Your Eating Habits...And to Find "Help" and "Happiness."

Change Your Eating Habits, Native Stealing Style

If you are concerned about the health of your family after reading this book you can make some positive changes. Don't feel helpless, because although you can't do everything at once, you can do something at once. However, if it's possible to make dramatic changes without total family rebellion by all means do so. But my experience in changing anything, and changing it effectively, is to do it gradually. Follow the example of a native when he steals from another tribe. He never picks up the item and runs away with it, because if he did that, he'd undoubtedly get caught. And he never tells anyone what he's about to do, because then everyone would start watching him too closely....He merely takes the intended item and moves it *just one inch at a time* towards his hut. The other tribe never notices the loss, because the loss is only in inches. However, because of the patience and perserverance of the thief he is able to steal many things without being caught....You must be like the native thief and change family eating habits IN INCHES, then you'll be effective.

Don't Announce What You're Doing

Don't make big announcements or advertise to your family what you're doing or it will increase the task. I know from experience....One evening my husband and children were shaking heavy amounts of pepper on their food and I boldy said, "I just read an article and it said that too much pepper inflames the stomach. I think we should all cut down." I was appalled as I watched one member of the family pour a fist full of pepper in his hand and throw all of it on his food, because IT WASN'T COMING OUT OF THE SHAKER FAST ENOUGH. He used so much pepper that his food and his plate turned BLACK! Now everyone at our house just loves pepper....I've since learned to keep mum. By the way kelp, a nutritious pepper-look-alike, works nicely and nobody is the wiser, except mother me. Remember—GO EASILY, and VERY QUIETLY.

How to Help!

There's one thing I'm certain of, in getting some positive changes. Public pressure is the secret and almost the only way to get prompt action. Many men in government today and those in charge of the nation's health are men that are heads of the major food industries. So you see, it's a vicious battle. However, I'm willing to fight for the rights and health of my family, as I know many of you are. Housewives could form committees, write to government officials and be heard. We could refuse on a wide scale to buy some of the unhealthy foods, and I promise you, that we'd get results. Start your own committees and go to work.

How to Get Some Help!

Almost every commercial food is drugged with something, unless otherwise stated. One organization that is trying to help the situation is The Ecological Food Society, 114 East 40th South St., New York City, 10016. For five dollars (several people could go in together), you can become a member, and from what I understand the money is well worth the investment. They'll send you a catalogue and newsletter and the money goes toward helping the food problem. It guarantees markets for organic foods (foods without harmful chemicals etc.) and possible outlets in your own areas. You also get many helps on caring for your own foods etc.

HAPPINESS IS. . . healthful life-giving foods; devotion to family; devotion to God; hard work; service to mankind; clean living habits; smiling often and having a cheerful attitude. When your life is balanced, you will no longer be searching for happiness, because you will find that wonderful inner peace dwelling within yourself.

—Appendix—

BIBLIOGRAPHY

Angier, Bradford, *Wilderness Cookery,* Stackpole Rubicon Books, Harrisburg, Pa., 1961.

"Beat Rising Food Prices, Make It Yourself," *Consumers Guide,* Skokie, Illinois, 1974.

Borsook, Henry, Ph.D., M.D., *Vitamins,* Pyramid Books, New York, N.Y., 1968.

Clark, Linda, *Stay Young Longer,* The Devon Adair, Old Greenwich, Conn.

"Composition of Foods," Agricultural Handbook No. 8, United States Department of Agriculture, Washington D. C.

Davis, Adele, *Let's Eat Right to Keep Fit,* New American Library, New York, N.Y., 1954.

Dickey, Esther, *Passport to Survival,* Bookcraft Inc., Salt Lake City, Utah, 1969.

Elwood, Catharyn, *Feel Like a Million,* Simon and Schuster, New York, N.Y., 1956.

Hunter, Beatrice Trum, *Consumer Beware,* Simon and Schuster, New York, N.Y., 1971.

Josephson, Elmer A., *God's Key to Health and Happiness,* Bible Spotlight Publications, Wichita, Kansas, 1962.

Kordel, LeLord, *Cook Right—Live Longer,* Award Books, New York, N.Y.

Lappe, Frances Moor, *Diet for a Small Planet,* Ballantine Books, New York, N.Y., 1971.

Lindlahr, Victor H., *You Are What You Eat,* Lancer Books, New York, N.Y., 1972.

Longgood, William, *The Poisons in Your Food,* Pyramid Books, New York, N.Y., 1960.

Marine, Gene and Van Allen, Judith, *Food Pollution, the Violation of Our Inner Ecology,* Holt, Rinehart and Winston, New York, Chicago and San Francisco, 1972.

Norris, P. E., *Everything You Want to Know about Honey,* Pyramid Books, New York, N.Y., 1970.

Rombauer, Irma S. and Becker, Marion Rombauer, *Joy of Cooking,* New American Library, New York, N.Y., 1931.

Rorty, James and Norman, N. Philip, M.D., *Bio-organics: Your Food and Your Health,* Lancer Books, New York, N.Y., 1956.

Rosenvall, Miller and Flack, *Wheat for Man...Why and How,* Bookcraft Inc., Salt Lake City, Utah, 1966.

Williams, Dr. Roger J., *Nutrition Against Disease,* Bantam Books Inc., New York, N.Y., 1971.

Winter, Ruth, *A Consumer's Dictionary of Food Additives,* Crown Publishers, New York, N.Y., 1972.

—————*Beware of the Foods You Eat,* Crown Publishers, New York, N.Y., 1971.

FOOTNOTES
Part I

1. *New York Times* in Harrison Wellford, *Snowing The Wind,* (Grossman Publishers, 1972) p. 132.

FOOTNOTES
Part II

1. Cathryn Elwood, *Feel Like A Million,* (New York: Simon & Schuster, 1956) p. 26.
2. Francis W. Pottenger, Jr., M.D., and Michael J. Walsh, M.Sc., F.R.I.C. "Open Forum on Milk," *Modern Nutrition,* July, 1970, in Linda Clark, *Stay Young Longer* (New York: Pyramid , 1968).
3. As in 1, p. 27.
4. "The Wulzen Calcium Syndrome in Guinea Pigs," *American Journal of Physical Medicine.* Vol. 34, No. 1. Feb., 1955.
5. Linda Clark, *Stay Young Longer.* p. 195.
6. *Ibid.*
7. DHEW Publication No (OCD) 73-15, The American Medical Association.
8. Adele Davis, *Let's Eat Right to Keep Fit* (New York: Signet, 1970) p. 228.
9. W. M. Marriott, *Infant Nutrition.* rev. P. C. Jeans (St. Louis: C. V. Mosley Company).

1. Cathryn Elwood, *Feel Like a Million.*
2. William MacNider, M.D. in Linda Clark, *Stay Young Longer.*

1. "Chronic Pyridozine Deficiency in the Rat," *Nutrition Review.* Vol. 13, No 4. Apr. 1955. p. 19.
2. Beatrice Trum Hunter. *Consumer Beware* (New York: Simon & Schuster, 1971) p. 225.
3. Marie Balsley, M. F. Brinks and E. W. Speckman, "Nutritional Value of Milk Compared with Filled and Imitation Milks." *American Journal of Clinical Nutrition.* Volume 22. No. 2. February 1969. p. 179.
4. David Sanford, "Unmilk, Cowing the Consumer," *New Republic.* Aug 10. 1968. p. 11.

1. Linda Clark, *Stay Young Longer.* p. 196
2. H. D. Cremer et al., "Dental Caries and Growth in Rats Fed Whole-Milk Powder with Increasing Lysine Deterioration." *Journal of Nutrition.* Vol 15 No. 4. Apr. 1962. p. 21.

1. Cheese and Cheese Products, Definitions and Standards. Part 19 Cheese Standards. p. 27.
2. F. J. Schlink, *Eat, Drink and Be Wary* (New York: Covici Friede, 1935) p. 294.

1. These two companies will sell small quantities of commercial culture or rennet. This is not an endorsement of their product or service. This is just to supply you with two outlets that are available.

Dairy Laboratories
2300 Locust Street
Philadelphia, Pa. 19103

Marshal Dairy Laboratory
14 Proudfit Street
Madison, Wis. 53703

2. As in 1.

1. Irma S. Rombauer and Marion Rombauer Becker, *Joy of Cooking* (Chicago: signet) p. 485.

1. Ruth Winter, *A Consumer's Dictionary of Food Additives* (New York: Crown Publishers, 1972) pp. 70, 83, 134, 211.
2. *Ibid.*, pp. 39, 71, 201.
3. Franklin Bicknell, M.D., *Chemicals in Food and in Farm Produce: Their Harmful Effects* (London: Faber and Faber, 1960) pp. 69-70.

1. Ray Sawyer, "Ice Cream (He's crossed out "ice cream" and added the word "poison"). *Natural Food and Farming Magazine*, Nov., 1958.

1. "Keep Eggs Fresh—At Least Two Years!" *Farm Journal*, December, 1964, p. 20.
2. "Stronger Shells," *Wisconsin State Journal*, Apr. 10, 1966.

FOOTNOTES

Part III

1. Charles E. Calverly and Thor M. Gullickson, "Cardiac Failure of Vitamin-Free Rations as Revealed by Electro Cardiograms," *Science* (Oct., 3, 1946) p. 312 from Linda Clark, *Stay Young Longer* (New York: Pyramid, 1968).
2. Ruth Winter, *A Consumer's Dictionary of Foods* (New York: Crown, 1972) p. 160.
3. *Ibid.*, p. 40.
4. Royal Lee, D.D.S., "Primary Cause of Disease," reprint Lee Foundation for Nutritional Research, Milwaukee, Wisconsin, in Linda Clark, *Stay Young Longer*.
5. Adelle Davis, *Let's Eat Right to Keep Fit* (New York: Harcourt, Brace, Jovanovich Inc., 1954).

1. Marguerite A. Constant, C. A. Elvehjem, Paul H. Philips and H. William Sievert, "Dental Caries in the Cotton Rat," *Journal of Nutrition*, Vol. 53 (May 1954) pp. 26-27.
2. Michael F. Jacobson, *Eater's Digest* (New York: Doubleday, 1972) pp. 186, 187.

FOOTNOTES
Part IV

1. Elmer A. Josephson, "God's Keys to Health and Happiness," *Bible Spotlight Pub.*, (Wichita) p. 32.
2. *American Agriculturists*, (May 1965) p. 27.
3. Beatrice Trum Hunter. *Consumer Beware* (New York: Simon and Schuster. 1971) p. 101.
4. Rigoberto Iglesias, M.D., Granville F. Knight, M.D., W. Coda Martin, M.D. and William E. Smith, M.D., "Possible Cancer Hazards Presented by Feeding Diethylstilbestrol to Cattle," Symposium on Mecicated Feeds, *New York Medical Encyclopedia*, 1956, p. 168 in Beatrice T. Hunter, *Consumer Beware*.
5. "Antibiotics in Food Held Bad for Heart," *The New York Times*, August 13, 1961.
6. M. R. Clarkson, Assoc. Administrator, Agriculture Research Service, U.S.D.A., before the Food and Drug and Cosmetic Law Section of the N.Y. Bar Association, N.Y. City, January 24, 1962.
7. As in 3. p. 131.
8. "Chopped Beef," *Consumer Bulletin*, (July 1963) p. 37.
9. As in 3. p. 131.
10. "City Accuses Butchers of Selling Hamburger Containing 90 percent Fat," *The New York Times*, February 7, 1962.
11. Beatrice T. Hunter, *Consumer Beware*, p. 132.
12. Elmer A. Josephson, *God's Key to Health and Happiness*. pp. 32.33.
13. *Ibid.*, pp. 32-36.
14. Meredith Corp., "Expansion in the '70's," *Successful Farming Journal* (Des Moines: March, 1972) p. 8.
15. *New York Times*, March 4, 1968.
16. Ralph Nader, "Don't Eat That Dog," *The New Republic* (Wash. D.C. March 18, 1972) pp. 12-13.
17. *Ibid.*
18. "Decline and Fill of the American Hot Dog," *Time Magazine*, Chicago, Ill. (Oct. 2, 1972) p. 86.
19. *Ibid.*
20. Dr. W. Lyinsky, *Science*, Wash. D.C. (Dec. 21, 1973).
21. N. Philip Norman. M.D and James Rorty. *Your Food and Your Health* (New York: Lancer) p. 294.
22. Tom Herman. "Chicken Cancer Called Widespread Enough to Pose 'Nightmare' for Poultry Industry." *Wall Street Journal* (February 10, 1970) p. 6
23. *Associated Press*. Wash. D.C. and *The New York Times*, January 26, 1970
24. Harrison Wellford. *Sowing the Wind* (New York. Grossman. 1972) p. 46
25. *Ibid.*, pp. 80 and 81.
26. *Ibid.*, p. 131.
27. As in 3
28. Ruth Winter. *Beware of the Foods You Eat* (New York: Crown. 1971) p. 114
29. Michael F. Jacobson. *Sowing the Wind*. pp. 206 207.

30. "Canned Tuna," *Consumer Research* (Nov., 1974) pp. 816-819.
31. *Consumer Research Magazine* (Oct. 1973) Wash., N.H., p. 127.
32. *Holy Bible,* King James Version.
33. *Ibid.*
34. Dr. P. E. Allson, *Problems in Athletic Conditioning* (Provo, Utah: Brigham Young University).
35. Ruth Winter, *Beware of the Foods You Eat,* p. 268.
36. Michael F. Jacobson, *Eater's Digest* (New York: Doubleday, 1972) pp. 186,-87.
37. Ruth Winter, *Beware of the Foods You Eat,* p. 155.
38. *Consumer Research Magazine* (October, 1973).
39. *Nation's Business,* Washington, D.C., Volume 61, No. 10 (October, 1973) p. 90.

FOOTNOTES

Part V

1. *Consumer Research Magazine* (Oct. 1973) p. 133.
2. Dr. O. W. Grussendorf, "Removing Pesticide Residues From Food," *Biodynamics.* No. 76 (Fall, 1965) pp. 28,29.
3. Reprint from FDA paper, June 1967, p. 2.
4. Bardman, Peterson and Warner, *Foundation for Enviornmental Biology,* (Berkeley: University of California, 1960).
5. "Tomatoes," *Consumer Bulletin,* (Oct. 1968) p. 42.
6. Mary E. Eheart. "Effect of Microwave Vs. Water-Blanching on Nutirients in Broccoli." *Journal of the American Dietetic Association* (Mar., 1967) p. 207.
7. Cathryn Elwood, *Feel Like a Million* (New York: Simon and Schuster, 1956) p. 269.
8. Dr. Werner Schuphan. *Nutritional Values in Crops and Plants, Problems for Producers and Consumers* (London: Faber and Faber, 1965) p. 178.
9. Beatrice T. Hunter, *Consumer Beware* (New York: Simon and Schuster, 1971) pp. 274, 275.
10. *Ibid.*
11. *Ibid.*
12. Ruth Winter. *Beware of the Foods You Eat.* (New York: Crown, 1971) p. 50.
14. "Stainless Steel Cooking Utensils." *Consumer Bulletin* (Oct., 1957).

FOOTNOTES

Part VI

1. *Ibid.,* Adelle Davis. p. 190 and Philip L. White. Sec. of the Council on Foods and Nutrition of the American Medical Association from the AMA publication. *Today's Health,* July. 1968
2. John T. Lichfield. Jr., M.D.. "Drug Toxicity in the Human Fetus and Newborn." *Applied Therapeutics.* September. 1967. pp. 922-926.
3. *Ibid.,* Ruth Winter, p. 69.
4. *Ibid.,* Gene Martin and Judith Van Allen. p. 146.
5. *National Enquirer.* Lantana. Florida. 33462.
6. *The Poisons in Your Food.* William Longgood. Simon and Schuster, 1960, p. 163.

7. *Consumer Bulletin Annual*, 1973, Washington, New Jersey
8. *Consumer Research Magazine*, October 1973, Washington, New Jersey, p. 127.
9. *Consumer Research Magazine*, Washington, New Jersey, Oct., 1973, p. 132.
10. *Ibid.*, Cathryn Elwood, p. 56. Compiled by Michael J. Walsh, M.Sc. American Foundation for Medical Dental Science, 251 So. Robertson, Beverly Hills, Calif.
11. *Everything You Want to Know About Honey*, P. E. Norris, Pyramid Books, New York, c. Carlson Wade, p. vii.
12. W. C. Heuper, M.D., "Are Sugars Carcinogens? An Experimental Study," *Cancer Research*, Vol. 25, No. 4, May 1965, p. 442.
13. *Ibid.*, Gene Marine and Judith Van Allen, p. 51-52.
14. *Consumer Bulletin Annual*, Washington, New Jersey, 1973, p. 5.
15. "Chewing Gum," *Consumer Bulletin*, Aug., 1961, p. 31.
16. *Ibid.*, Gene Marine and Judith Van Allen, p. 347.
17. *Ibid.*, p. 130.
18. *Ibid.*, Beatrice Trum Hunter, p. 188.
19. "Canadians Doubt That All peanuts Are Safe to Eat," *Health Bulletin*, Jan., 22, 1966, p. 1.
20. Lelord Kordel, *Cook Right—Live Longer*, Award Books, N.Y., N.Y., p. 46.
21. *Consumer Research Magazine*, Wash., N.H., Oct., 1973, p. 131.
22. Clive M. McKay, Ph.D., *Testimony* 81st Congress, 1st session, Hearings before the House Select Committee to investigate the Use of Chemicals in Food Products, 1950, pp. 90-109.
23. Howard J. Sanders, "Chemical Mutagens, The Road to Genetic Disaster?" *Chemical and Engineering News*, June 2, 1969, pp. 60-61.
24. *Ibid.*, Ruth Winter, p. 51.
25. B. T. Hunter, "DEP, Another Officially Sanctioned Cancer Inciter in Our Food," *Consumer Bulletin*, April, 1972.
26. *Ibid.*, Gene Marine and Judith Van Allen, p. 53.
27. "Mineral Oil," *Consumer Bulletin*, Dec. 1966, p. 42.
28. *Ibid.*, Adelle Davis, p. 46.
29. *Consumer Research Magazine*, Oct. 1973, p. 130.
30. *Ibid.*, Michael F. Jacobson, Doubleday and Co. Inc., Garden City, New York, 1972.
31. *Ibid.*

Appendix

INDEX

INDEX (Cont.)

Appendix

INDEX (Cont.)

INDEX (Cont.)